PIPPA S1

CU00656774

UNIVERSITY
AND
CHRONIC
ILLNESS
A SURVIVAL GUIDE

PIPPA STACEY

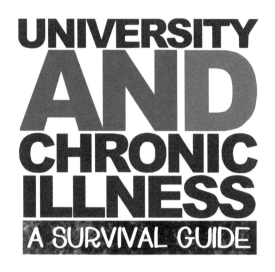

UNIVERSITY **AND** CHRONIC ILLNESS
A SURVIVAL GUIDE

DAISA & CO
Est. 2003

University and Chronic Illness: A Survival Guide published in Great Britain in 2020

Written by Pippa Stacey
Copyright © Pippa Stacey 2020

A CIP catalogue record for this book is available from the British Library

ISBN 978-1-9162251-2-1

Book Cover Design by: Daisa & Co Publishing.
Bespoke illustrations by Hannah Ensor of Stickman Communications

Book typeset by:
DAISA & CO PUBLISHING
Barton Upon Humber
North Lincolnshire
United Kingdom
DN18 5JR
www.daisapublishing.com

Printed in England

Daisa & Co Publishing is committed to a sustainable future for our business, our readers and our planet, promoting responsible management of forest resources.

For every chronically ill person who thinks their hard work goes unnoticed.

Your time is coming.

Contents

Introduction

Well, hello! If you're reading this, the chances are you're thinking about going to university. Either that, or you're simply wondering why all former students seem lost for words whilst trying to describe their own university experiences. Whether you identify as chronically ill or not, it's safe to say that these upcoming years could become some of the most memorable of your life.

Making the decision to become a student is a big step for any young person to take. It marks the beginning of your independent adult life and could form the foundation blocks of your future career as well. However, as I'm sure you, dear reader, know all too well, living with long-term illness means that decisions like these have to be made very carefully.

I know that this time in your life may be full of questions and uncertainties...

- o Is university the right choice for me?
- o What kind of course should I choose?
- o Would it be best to live at home or move away?
- o How do I manage studying on top of day-to-day living?
- o What kind of support am I entitled to?
- o Will my flatmates understand my situation?

o   And, most importantly, how on Earth do I fit all these pyjamas into just one drawer?

Disabled young people are increasingly being encouraged to pursue education and employment, but I think we can all agree there's a remarkable lack of support out there for us. And personally, I reckon that the guidance that *does* exist often only addresses the academic aspects of university, rather than the overall student experience. In my eyes, this reflects the fact that much of the information out there isn't coming from chronically ill people themselves.

Therefore, my hope is that this book will become your very own chatty guide, one that goes beyond your typical standardised advice on academics and job prospects, and instead encompasses all aspects of student life. We'll discuss socialising, independent living, managing your money, what to do when things go wrong, and so much more.

I'd like to empower prospective students to make informed decisions, to think about some of the important questions that often go unspoken about, and guide you through the process right from the beginning. We'll go through everything from student support plans to personal care checklists, accessible revision tips to quick and easy meal ideas.

And ultimately, I hope to show that with the right preparation and support in place, going to university with a chronic illness isn't only possible, but could be one of the best experiences of your life.

A bit about me

So, who on Earth is this person and why are they advising me? Before we go any further, let me introduce myself…

I'm Pippa, and I have a long-term chronic illness. I studied BSc Psychology in Education at the University of York and graduated with an honours degree in 2016. Although I didn't know it at the time, I'd been mildly ill with my condition as a teenager, with symptoms developing only slowly and without having a significant impact on day-to-day life. However, towards the end of my first year of university, my health massively declined, and I suffered a relapse. It's safe to say that it wasn't a particularly joyful time in my life, and it was at this point that I first started identifying as chronically ill and disabled.

My way of life changed massively from here onwards, but with support and adjustments, fortunately I was just about able to continue studying full-time and living away from home. During the final year of my studies I also became an ambulatory wheelchair user, with

George Ezra, the wobbly transit wheelchair, becoming the established sixth member of our student house. Finding humour in my situation was an important coping mechanism for me but, as I'm sure you can imagine, surviving university life with an unrelenting chronic illness wasn't without its challenges.

Personally, I think it's crucial that anybody in a similar position to me can access this kind of advice, knowing it's coming from somebody who's been through the process themselves and who genuinely understands. In writing this book, I hope to share with you all the things I wish somebody had told me back then, so that you too can have the most sustainable and rewarding student experience possible.

A Short Caveat/ Disclaimer

Before we jump right into it, let me emphasise that not every chronically ill or disabled person is going to be well enough to pursue higher education. Regardless of your specific impairment, chronic illness ranges widely in severity, and no two individuals are affected in the same way. A person's level of disability falls on a spectrum: something that should be kept in mind in every conversation we have about chronic illness and education.

Therefore, I hope the information and advice offered in this book is taken with a pinch of salt. The last thing on Earth I would want is for a well-meaning friend or relative to pick up this book and use it as ammunition for 'encouraging' somebody to consider university when it simply isn't right for them. If you're the well-meaning friend or relative reading this right now, my advice would be to put down this book, be an ally, and go and source a packet of their favourite biscuits for them instead. Being chronically ill is a full-time job in itself: there is absolutely no shame in not pursuing higher education, or in making the difficult decision to withdraw from studying. Health and wellbeing should always, always come first.

That said, for those who have made an informed decision and are preparing to become a student, this one is for you. At the very least, I hope the following information combined with my own experiences form a baseline set of resources that you can adapt to suit your own circumstances, and I *really* hope we can have some fun with it along the way too.

So, let's get on with it, shall we?

Chapter One
CHOOSING A DEGREE

So, let's kick this journey off with deciding what on earth you'd like to study.

For some people, the decision will have come easily; they'll have already found the subject they want to pursue, researched relevant courses of study and found some favourites, and they'll be chomping at the bit, ready to hit the application forms. For others, the decision will take much more consideration.

For starters, get yourself online and set aside some time specifically for researching courses of interest. Make a note of anything and everything that sparks your interest; there'll be plenty of time to mull them over and narrow down your choices later on. As well as all your typical markers of success, such as league tables and student satisfaction surveys, there are also several course elements to consider from a chronic illness perspective…

1. Contact hours

The time spent physically in university can vary massively between different courses. A subject like History may have as few as four contact hours a week, with the rest of the time allocated to independent study, whereas a science degree may be almost entirely comprised of 9am-5pm days of lectures and practical sessions.

If your condition means you find it difficult to leave the house regularly or for sustained periods, or if you need time to recover after being out and about, give some thought to how many contact hours you can reasonably manage per week; not how many you can physically do by pushing yourself, but how many you can comfortably sustain on a long-term basis. There may be some wiggle room with your contact hours or work week (and we'll get to this later), but it's important to consider things as they stand, regardless.

2. <u>Practical vs non-practical study</u>

More food for thought - how much of the course is made up of practical, physical activities, versus how much is written? Again, science subjects may be culpable here. I distinctly remember my (non-disabled) friends telling us about their 'labs'; 9am-5pm days on their feet, conducting experiments and practical work. For disciplines such as Geography or Environment Studies, there may be mandatory field trips to accommodate, and if you're studying for a caring profession, there may be assessed work experience and placements necessary for your qualification too.

Again, these things may be negotiable and adjustable further down the line, but if you already know that your present state of health means they're an absolute no-no, then it may be wise to consider theory-based subjects as well.

However, for practical subjects, it may be that there are reasonable adjustments that can be made. We'll discuss these further in later chapters, but for now let's hear from **Katherine** who made use of a lab assistant to meet the requirements of her Science degree:

'Because of my chronic illness, the practical aspect of my degree was the part that I was the most apprehensive about. Some programmes will have more lab time than others, and for certain courses you will have to complete a set number of hours of practical work to graduate. For example, Chemistry degrees that are accredited by The Royal Society of Chemistry have a lot of lab work; six hours per week during your first year, increasing to nine and then twelve during your second and third years. This is something that you will be able to find out from the course prospectus before you apply.

My personal accommodations for laboratory work were always having a stool available to sit if required, as well as access to a lab teaching assistant for assessed practical work that I was unable to carry out myself. I was also exempt from attending residential fieldwork courses. All of these adjustments were outlined in my Personal Learning Plan (PLP) by my Disability Advisor prior to me starting the course.

For most practical work you will be able to sit on a stool, and if there is any heavy lifting, a lab technician can do that for you. My lab work was always conducted in pairs or small groups, and I found arranging to be paired with a friend who understood my requirements helped me to work to the best of my ability. If there is a practical assessment that you cannot do because of your disability, your university will be able to provide you with an alternative assessment, or you will be able to dictate to your lab teaching assistant who will carry out the lab work under your instruction.

Different universities will have different policies, but it is possible to find out what accommodations they can give you with regards to practical work before you apply by contacting the course leader or disability office. Fortunately, I found that my POTS was not a barrier with regards to practical work, and I enjoyed my science degree greatly.'

3. Exams vs coursework

One final area to consider is good old exams and coursework, the written tasks that will likely determine your academic grades. The majority of degrees will typically involve at least one exam of some kind, but the ratio of exams to coursework again can vary.

If you're somebody who struggles with brain-fog or finds it difficult to retain information, you may be inclined to choose a degree where coursework forms the majority of your final result. It's also worth bearing in mind that exams and coursework can exist in various forms, so I'd strongly advise researching these areas in advance.

As an example, some of my friends had to do 'timed-essays'. They would receive an unknown assessment question that counted towards their final grade, with the instruction to submit their work in exactly 24 hours' time.

A typical student's approach to this scenario, as you can imagine, would be stocking up on energy drinks, not sleeping at all until it was over, and having a mild existential crisis at 3am.

This type of devilish assessment is designed to test particular skills, but as you can imagine, it isn't chronic illness-friendly in the slightest. Processes such as these highlight just how important it is to be aware of examination methods in advance.

Whilst you're unlikely to find in-depth guidance on the issues mentioned here online, on general course search websites, there are alternative ways you could glean this information ahead of choosing the courses you apply for. You could contact the relevant department at each potential university and ask to speak to the course leader, or you could do this via each institution's Disability Services team. If you're currently at a college or sixth form which has a careers teacher, they may be able to assist with this too.

The questions highlighted above are all important to consider, especially if you have additional needs, but first and foremost, do ensure you're choosing a course that you *want* to study. If you're going to devote three years of your life to something, you want to ensure it's in an area that you'll genuinely enjoy and get something out of. Think about things carefully, but (bear with me, horrifyingly cheesy line approaching) … follow your heart. And remember, if things don't work out the way you hope they will, there could be the option to change courses at a later date too.

My Experience

Not too many people know that I actually switched degree courses part-way through my very first term at university. I was originally studying BSc Psychology, but quickly realised I wasn't enjoying the theoretical content that made up most of the course.

Instead, I did some research and found the BSc Psychology in Education programme at the same university: still an accredited psychology degree that covered the essentials, but with much more emphasis on applied knowledge in practice.

As I already had the grades I needed, I arranged a meeting with my academic supervisor to discuss my desire to transfer, then on their instruction wrote an application email to the head of my desired new programme. Within no time, I was accepted on the course and attending my first new lecture, not too far behind the rest of the group.

Bish bash bosh.

Chapter Two
CHOOSING A UNIVERSITY

Now, choosing a degree and choosing a university often fall hand in hand, and there isn't necessarily a correct order to go about these.

There's no joy in finding a course you love at a university you're not fully happy with, and vice versa. Choosing your second home for the next however many years is such an important part of your university journey, so I'd spend some time contemplating the following areas...

1. <u>Traditional university vs online learning?</u>

Whilst this book is tailored towards those attending traditional universities, do remember that online learning is an option too. You can study for a variety of degrees from the comfort of your own home, and not just with the Open University; many institutions also offer their own online learning schemes, meaning that on completion, you still graduate with a degree from that specific university.

There are pros and cons to traditional universities and online learning, but one assumption which may not necessarily be correct is that online learning is inherently more inclusive or accessible. Online learning *is* ultimately more flexible; you can choose your own hours to fit around your health needs, change your plans when you need to, and work fully independently. However this can mean the level of pastoral and academic support is compromised. Think carefully about your own learning style as well as your circumstances, and if in doubt, talk to others who've experienced either mode of learning in your subject area.

For starters, let's hear from **Sarah**, a chronically ill former student who I chatted to about her own positive experiences of studying with the Open University:

Hi Sarah! Tell us a bit about yourself...
I have ME/CFS and I graduated with a degree in Open Science in 2008. I enjoy reading, learning and losing myself in a good book, and The OU has enabled me to pursue my love of learning.

What made you decide to study with the Open University? Did you consider traditional universities, or was studying online an easy decision for you?
As a working, single mum, I thought that 'normal' University wasn't an option for me, practically or financially, especially since I struggle with maths. I thought the OU's science module sounded so interesting, plus I

could study from home with support being only a phone call away. I decided to tentatively apply, and not only did I get onto the course, I also qualified for financial assistance. This meant that in February the following year, I received a box packed full of textbooks and materials. The feeling of opening that box still resonates today – I was so excited! It was the best decision I've made.

At what point did you first declare your condition? Did you seek or experience any additional support from the programme at this stage?

I developed ME/CFS about halfway through my degree. It took me a year to realise I had it, and then a further year to get diagnosed. However, all the complicating factors in my life that led me to The OU – kid, 2 jobs, life – meant that I had already learnt one of the most valuable tools someone with ME/CFS can have; time management. I informed my tutor about my condition and they were really supportive, advising I didn't have to finish if I couldn't quite make it that year. They took that pressure off me with no judgement and it gave me that release of expectation: it actually enabled me to break through, emotionally and mentally, and I sat my final exams with confidence.

In a nutshell, how was your overall experience of studying in this way? What kind of adjustments and support were available to you?

I can only speak in a positive way about The OU and distance learning from home – the materials and support were consistently of the best quality. On the occasions I did need help, I was greeted with acceptance and flexibility – both pre and post illness – mainly in the form of understanding and supportive tutors.

After finishing my degree, I became aware of the Disability Support Programme they run. After such a fulfilling experience, I really wanted to pay it forward, so I started, and continue, donating to the programme every month. Reading about how other students are now thriving on accessible courses is really satisfying.

There are undoubtedly lots of positives for chronically ill people studying online, but were there any drawbacks? How did you overcome these?

I was able to attend the majority of my course's tutor groups, but as my ME/CFS progressed, I found that this was no longer an option. However, I was still able to connect with my tutor over the phone and receive the support I needed, and there were forums and chat groups with other students accessible online too. Therefore, I never felt excluded, and this helped me to get through the last year in particular.

Being chronically ill is all about finding the adjustment that works best for you – and studying is no exception.

If you could give any piece of advice to somebody considering studying with the Open University, what would it be?

Call the OU, have the conversation, and see what sort of journey you can take with them. Ensure you both have realistic goals and expectations as it is a two-way street and remember that communication is key. Go for it – you've got nothing to lose and perhaps everything to gain.

Thanks so much for sharing your experiences, Sarah!

My Experience

I made a conscious decision to focus this book only on my undergraduate degree in a traditional university, but I will mention that afterwards I pursued an online Master's degree with a reputable university, studying Health Psychology… and found it so inaccessible that I decided not to continue.

Even though studying from home in a flexible way was a huge benefit, the lack of information and support for disabled students, even when I raised this with my personal supervisor (who barely knew my name), combined with the disorganisation and discrepancies within the programme, played a large role in my decision to first take a leave of absence, and then later permanently withdraw from the programme. This meant that I studied for only one year instead of two, and graduated with a postgraduate diploma rather than a Master's degree.

Obviously, every institution is different, and all have strengths and weaknesses, but personally I was surprised to have found my experiences of a traditional university setting much more accessible than online learning. It just goes to show how important it is to challenge your initial assumptions, do your research, and wherever possible, speak with others about their experiences too.

2. Full time or part time study?

When deciding whether to study full-time or part-time, there are a fair few factors to take into consideration. First of all, look at how many contact hours you have per week. Even if this number seems low to you, remember that the general rule of thumb is that for every contact hour you have, the aim is to be doing another two hours of independent study alongside it. Whether or not any student actually achieves this is a *whole* other debate, but that's the intention.

It can be so easy to think, 'Ah it'll be fine, I'll go for full-time hours and power through', especially when you're full of motivation and eager to get started. Believe me, I've been there. However, think of your future self in week 8 of term, who may live to resent this decision.

As I mentioned earlier, my best advice would be not to think how much you can 'manage' in a week, but rather, how much you can comfortably do. Burning yourself out early on and struggling through isn't the answer here, especially when you take into consideration that you'll likely be living independently for the first time as well.

Working little and often over a longer period of time is much more effective than aiming for single big bursts that take longer to recover from.

Remember your pacing, and if you feel even the slightest twinge of anxiety at the thought of a typical week of study, I'd advise not taking the risk. Your future self will thank you for it.

Now, that's all well and good, but I'd be an absolute hypocrite if I sat here and said that I myself listened to my body and dropped down to part-time study when I felt that I needed to. I think we all know that it's much easier to dole out well-intentioned advice to others than actually listen to it ourselves.

Instead, let me briefly mention how reasonable adjustments might come into play here. Whilst I did continue studying full-time, I had an agreement with my university that I wouldn't attend contact hours if I was more capable of working from home instead. In practice, what that meant was that whilst I was still technically studying full-time, I did much of my work from home rather than physically attending lectures and tutorials. I had access to lecture slides and made notes to study from and kept in regular contact with staff to ensure my learning was on track, even when most of my day was spent in bed. And most importantly, I could self-motivate with tea and biscuits without the judgement of those around me. One biscuit for every paragraph is the rule of thumb, right?

Again, you'll need to think carefully about how your mode of study or contact hours would work for you and your circumstances, and it could be valuable to discuss this with your tutors beforehand, and see whether alternate arrangements would be feasible: it's important to give yourself as many options as possible.

3. Home or away?

When you're researching universities, it can seem like the world is your oyster. There are hundreds of places of study in cities up and down the country, and in theory, you could become a part of any one of them. The million-dollar question is, would it be best to stick closer to home or stray further away?

One thing that seemed to irk people when I previously did some writing on university and chronic illness was the suggestion to stay closer to home if you had complex health needs. And to an extent, it initially irked me too: if the world was truly accessible and accommodating, disabled and chronically ill people should have the freedom of choice to study anywhere they like, the same as their non-disabled peers. The idea of somebody having to compromise on anything, simply because of their disability, has never sat right with me.

However, I will say this: of the five universities I applied to, two were relatively close to home, one was middling, and two were literally at the opposite end of the country. And after I became ill, all I can say is I'm so relieved that I opted for one that was only an hour away from home. There were situations I couldn't possibly have foreseen when I first went off to university as a non-disabled student, and I'm not exaggerating when I say that if my parents hadn't been able to get to me when I had no choice but to ask for help, I probably would've had to cease living away from home after I became ill.

So take this guidance with a pinch of salt; it might be that you have a good grip on your needs already, you're aware of support and facilities in the area you're hoping to move to, and maybe you even have family or contacts locally who you know you can call upon in case of emergency. If that's the case, go for your life: move wherever you'd like to, and enjoy the heck out of it. However, if you do have uncertainties, sit down with your family and think about what would be best for all of you.

Alternatively, you may decide that living at home rather than moving into student accommodation is the best option for you. Even if doing so would involve commuting to and from contact hours, it may still be that the home-environment that you're used to and may even be specially adapted for you is most suitable.

4.   How are the location and local amenities?

Regardless of your distance from home, it goes without saying that your location whilst studying will have a significant impact on your day-to-day experience. And whilst the Pizza Hut-to-pedestrian ratio isn't *quite* as valid a reason to determine your new home, whether or not you personally feel you belong in the area absolutely is. If you're going for a bigger city, you may have the benefit of a good public transport network to cut down on walking distances, but it may lack a community feel. A smaller town or coastal university may offer a calmer, less 'studenty' experience, but lack inclusive amenities and facilities, such as wheelchair accessible shops and restaurants. Before making your choices and applying, I would always advise spending a day or two in the potential area, to get a feel for it. Could you see yourself living there?

Open Days

There are various ways to approach all of the above questions, but Open Days are an excellent starting point for scoping out various universities and what they have to offer. You can walk around the campus and see facilities for yourselves, speak to staff and faculty members, and pick the brains of current students. I'd strongly recommend seeking out disability advisors or other pastoral/support faculty members, as they will be best placed to inform you about any specific issues related to being a disabled student.

There's always a really lovely atmosphere during Open Days, with so many prospective students excited to explore what could be their future home. However, if you'd prefer a calmer, more tailored experience, you may be able to book an individual appointment to either be shown around particular universities, or look around them yourself. Although this approach, being outside of organised Open Days, may remove the opportunity to speak with more people, it can feel much less overwhelming to those prone to anxiety or cognitive overload.

Go prepared with a list of questions or your requirements. There's no shame in making notes whilst you're there either. I remember taking some short videos on my phone; these can give you a clearer visual reminder of how it was once you've left, so you're not just relying on memories... especially when good old brain-fog can make that a bit of a problematic system to start with.

<u>Potential questions to ask at Open Days, tailored for chronically ill students:</u>

o What does the university look for in an applicant? Do you have equality and diversity policies?

o How safe and secure is the campus/ university area? Is there pastoral or medical support nearby?

o What's it like to live in this town or city? What do you wish you had known before you had moved here?

o Do you have many part-time students, and how are they supported?

o What support is available for disabled students? Where can I find out more?

o In your opinion, what's the best and worst part of being a student here?

Chapter Three
THE APPLICATION PROCESS

So now you have a better idea of what the heck you're doing with your life for the next however many years, it's time to show off your skills and earn your place...

<u>How to apply</u>

Step One: UCAS

In the UK, we have a delightful system that goes by the name of UCAS. Not to be confused with another undiagnosed medical condition, the acronym UCAS stands for Universities and Colleges Admissions Service, and allows you to apply for up to five courses through online forms and a personal statement. Your decisions also arrive through that same system, making it, in essence, a simple and streamlined process.

However, getting the application and personal statement right is a critical part of ensuring you receive the offers you deserve, and it's also here where you can first choose to disclose your disability or condition. Now, as I mentioned, I didn't actually identify as chronically ill when I was applying to university myself, meaning that I may not be best placed to advise on this part of the process. Instead, let me hand you over to Welfare Officer **Lorna Reeve**, who kindly agreed to chat with me and share her insights into the UCAS process as both an advisor and a chronically ill person herself…

Hi Lorna! Tell us a bit about yourself…

I've just graduated from a Psychology degree at Durham University. I have a number of conditions causing mental health issues, chronic pain, fatigue and autonomic issues, and ended up using a powered wheelchair during my degree.

Whilst at University, I was a Welfare Officer for our Students with Disabilities Association where I aimed to support students as well as represent them and make changes to the culture around disability at Durham.

Durham is collegiate, so I was also my college's Disabilities Representative for a year and Assistant Welfare Officer for another along with a few other things I got involved in! I'm also a Crisis Volunteer for Shout, the UK's first crisis text line, and an advisor for Young Minds as well as a member of Student Minds' Student Advisory Committee. I like being busy!

For those with chronic illnesses, the application process for university can seem lengthy and overwhelming. Do you have any tips for how to tackle it head-on?

Applications are always so complicated, and it can feel like we're being judged at every turn. I would recommend starting your application as early as possible and to go through it in small chunks. I also found it invaluable to have someone else check the whole thing for accuracy, whether that be a teacher, friend or family member. It's always worth making sure brain-fog hasn't struck without you noticing!

The personal statement section of UCAS applications is often the first opportunity applicants have to really show their worth. What advice would you give to a chronically ill student writing their personal statement?

I'd say definitely write your personal statement in a word document and take time over it – there's no need to expect it to be perfect straight away but equally it's not worth agonising over it for so long it makes you ill. As with the whole application form, have someone read over it for you. Some people include their chronic illness in their personal statement, so if it fits, explains things or if you just want to add it in, it could be something to consider.

Personally, I didn't- my own personal statement focused on the degree areas I was most interested in and how my A levels and extra-curricular stuff would help this (interestingly, my favourite parts have changed massively through my degree!).

My references for university did include that I had chronic illnesses, because it had affected my AS level grades. Basically, my form tutor was writing my reference and pointed out that my AS level grades (A in the subject I dropped and ABC in the ones I continued to A level) didn't line up with my predicted grades (A's) and it might make universities overlook my application (particularly as I was considering applying to Oxford). My health struggles have always affected exam seasons, so this really helped me feel more comfortable and able to focus on doing as well as possible in my exams, whilst also not compromising the point I wanted to make in my own personal statement.

The application form is often the first place where prospective students can choose to disclose their disability, but many people worry they will be discriminated against because of their health condition. Are there any words of wisdom you could offer here?

You'll probably see different advice everywhere on if, and when, and how to disclose. My best advice would be to think about your choice. My personal choice is to disclose conditions on your application form, simply because it can help you access the best support. I actually identified as having a chronic illness before going to university but didn't really identify as disabled, meaning ticking the box felt slightly wrong to me, but it meant I could get the support I needed early on.

Almost every University has a peer group of disabled students, including those with chronic illnesses, and a lot of our work is in changing the university culture with less discrimination and making things more accessible. In my role, I spoke to people who hadn't disclosed their condition to the University in any way, which is your legal right not to, but meant there were more limited support options for their studying (remember, you can still speak to charities and other organisations about your conditions without disclosing to anyone at university). I chose to disclose on my application form because it meant my university contacted me to organise a meeting as soon as possible and I could plan things in advance.

If you could give three take-home tips to a chronically ill student filling in their application form, what would they be?

- o *Try not to overthink the content, just make sure it's accurate.*
- o *Make a decision on whether to disclose – this will be your own personal choice but do remember you can disclose at any point after the application form too.*
- o *Make your personal statement 'personal', include the things most important to you and make them relevant to the course you're applying for!*

Step Two: Interviews and Assessments

For particular courses, offers can be made on the basis of an application alone. For others, you may be required to attend an interview or assessment centre before a decision is made. Again, I was one of the lucky beans who didn't have to attend any interviews myself, but I can appreciate the additional factors you would need to consider in order to navigate this process alongside chronic illness. Fortunately, Disabled Students Advisor **Melanie Thorley** has some words of wisdom to share here...

Hi Melanie! Do tell us a bit about you and your background...

I work as a disability outreach officer at the University of Greenwich, working across London and the South East. I have been in the role for 12 years and love my work. As I have been a disabled student myself (depression and fibromyalgia) I have first-hand experience of studying at university with two disabilities. My mental health crashed in my last semester of my undergraduate sociology degree and I had to interrupt my doctorate for two years when I was put on morphine patches for pain relief. Thankfully, I finished them both, and now use my experiences assisting others and ensuring they make the most of their own time at university.

My work also includes employing University of Greenwich disabled students as STAART Ambassadors – working with prospective and current disabled students. Seeing my ambassadors graduate is the best bit of my job.

For chronically ill prospective students, the thought of an interview can feel daunting. What steps could people take to help them prepare?

o *Apply to a university signed up to the Disability Confident kitemark. More information on this scheme can be found on the Disability Confident website.*

o *The university should ask if you would like any adjustments for your interview. You could ask for an interview close to the main entrance of the building, on the ground floor. If any computers or technical equipment will be used in the interview, you can request any assistive technology you may need.*

o *Ask other disabled students who have already been through the process if they have any tips or advice. You may be able to find people online through social media or support networks, and most will likely be glad to assist.*

o *Ensure you have plenty of rest in the days leading up to the interview and stay hydrated. If it hasn't already been mentioned, it may be worth enquiring in advance whether you can take water bottles, medication or any other essentials into the interview with you.*

o *You could bring someone with you to wait outside, if it would ease your worries. Again, if you would benefit from having a companion with you, be sure to discuss this with your point of contact in advance.*

If somebody were to experience an adverse medical event during their actual interview, for example if they were to suddenly feel unwell, what would be the best thing to do in that immediate situation?

Do not panic. Most admission tutors will have experienced this before. Ask for a ten-minute break, go outside, take deep breaths, engage any strategies you have to calm yourself. If you cannot recover, it is acceptable to request another interview, and doing so will not harm your chances of gaining an offer.

Is there one overarching piece of advice you could give to chronically ill prospective students who have been offered an interview?

It can help to remember that admissions tutors do not see your entire application – they have no idea of your gender, age, ethnicity, disability etc. All they receive is your personal statement and qualifications (if appropriate). This means the tutor thinks your application is a strong one. You have the skills and/or knowledge for this degree otherwise you would not have been granted an interview. So with that in mind, do your best and go for it!

Step Three: The Waiting Game

You've submitted your applications, bossed your interviews and assessments, and you're well and truly on a roll. So, what happens next?

Well... waiting is what happens next, and usually a fair bit of it. Academic course leaders have months to decide who they would like on their programme, meaning that it could be a long while before you hear anything back, particularly if you applied earlier in the academic year.

Universities and courses can vary massively in their average decision-making time, so don't feel disheartened if you see others getting one offer after another and you're still staring at an empty inbox.

I got my first offer within three weeks of submitting my application, but didn't get my York offer, the one I was holding out for, until months and months later. Seriously not the time to be playing hard to get, York, but I suppose I forgive you.

Your offer will either be conditional or unconditional. If you're currently in sixth form or taking exams, you'll likely receive conditional offers; places subject to you meeting specific grade requirements on your upcoming exams. If you're a mature student or returning to education after time off, you may already have the grades you need and be given an unconditional offer instead.

Sometimes, you may be made what's known as an alternate offer, or an offer with alternate conditions to the entry requirements listed when you applied. I had one offer made with alternate conditions thanks to the A-Level subjects I was taking, with lower grades necessary to secure a place, but I imagine these offers could, in theory, be made on the basis of significant health conditions too.

Step Four: Accepting and Declining Your Offers

If you take one thing away from this section, let it be this: try not to accept or decline anything until you've had a response from every course you applied to. It can be so tempting to get excited and 'firm' one of your offers as soon as it comes in, particularly if it's for your first-choice course, but hold the heck back and wait. You never know what could happen.

Once you've heard back from all your chosen courses, you can choose your firm (first) choice and your insurance (second) choice. Your insurance choice could hold particular importance when you're a chronically ill student; if there are two universities you love but have the same entry requirements, it doesn't really make sense to use them both for your firm and insurance choice. If you don't make the grades for one, you won't make the grades for the other, and you therefore risk being left with no confirmed place at all on results day. No matter how confident you feel in your future exam results, consider choosing one of your lower entry requirements courses to be your insurance choice. That's what it's there for: to be a back-up. Nothing is set in stone until results day comes around, and you can always change your mind again on the day.

If you find you have no offers at the application stage, or you've decided to decline the offers you received, there's no need to panic: UCAS Extra allows you to apply for one additional course online. Sometimes our circumstances change, particularly with a fluctuating health condition, so it's worth knowing that there could be one more chance for you. More information on this process can always be found on the UCAS website.

Results Day

If there's ever an overwhelming day in your life, it's results day. Even now, I can distinctly remember the days leading up to the moment that would decide the course of my life for the next three years; lying awake in bed the night before, hearing my alarm go off in the morning and feeling like I hadn't slept a wink. And that was *before* 'painsomnia' became a regular part of my chronically ill life.

My advice would be to keep yourself distracted as much as possible in the weeks leading up to your results: the day before, I remember calling on my best friend and making her sit on the floor whilst I plaited and unplaited her hair over and over; y'know, that well-known productive coping mechanism. It would be naïve to simply tell somebody not to worry, but for what it's worth, remember that you're going to be fine. Whatever happens, the world will keep on turning, and you *will* be okay.

The UCAS Track system for offers and acceptances tends to go live in the morning, and all being well, you'll be able to see your university decision even before you find out your grades. I'd recommend making sure you have your username and password at hand and ready to log-in with on the morning, so you're not flapping around in desperation and cursing your past self once the system first goes live. If you have the outcome you're hoping for, amazing! If not, no need to panic. It's time to pick up your results and decide what's to happen next.

If you haven't made the grades you need and haven't received an acceptance, you can use UCAS Clearing to apply for courses that still have places remaining. There should be somebody at your college or sixth form available on your results day who can assist you through this process. Otherwise, you can find further information on how to proceed on the UCAS website.

Back in the day, somebody thought that handing out white envelopes containing people's grades in a confined space would be the best system for results day. As you can imagine, having an abundance of anxious young people dealing with potentially stressful situations can make for quite an overwhelming environment. My best advice would be not to get swept up in it: find yourself a quiet corner and allow yourself to sit with your thoughts and feelings. You're not obliged to share your results or plans with anybody unless you want to, and calmly assessing your options and deciding on your course of action is much more efficient and less energy-consuming than having a public meltdown in the common room.

But don't just take it from me. Read on to meet the lovely **Charli**, who recently picked up her own results...

My name is Charli and I got my A Level results in August 2019. I studied History, Chemistry and Philosophy and Ethics, as well as an Extended Project Qualification.

Results Day was such a nerve-wracking experience and in hindsight, I wish I'd looked after myself better before, during and after.

Here are my tips for chronically ill young people waiting on their own results:

- o *Have a plan. If you go through Clearing, you won't have long to accept - likely a day at most. If you need access arrangements or accommodation adaptations, it's worth finding out how well various different universities could accommodate you. This might be those you visited when making your original choices, looking at others' websites, or asking for a chat with the disability team if you do end up making Clearing calls.*
- o *Do what **you** need to do. There's a lot of pressure to open your envelope a certain way with your friends and teachers surrounding you. If you need to take your envelope outside then go back in, do that. If you want to just go home, do that. Similarly, if you need to take someone with you, feel free, or if you need to sit on the floor, don't be afraid to; even if photos are being taken or there's other stuff going on – there's no need to suffer for others' aesthetics.*
- o *Practice self-care throughout the whole period – and not just with generic face masks or a bubble bath (although those are nice and might help!). Make sure you keep up to date with therapy or*

medication and ask for support when you need it. Even during the tougher moments, simply changing your pyjamas might help you feel a bit better.

o *And though no-one wants to hear this before they get their grades, because it genuinely does feel like they're the most important thing, remember that there is truly more to life. You have so many years beyond this, and so much more to give. The education system isn't really built for us and everyone is so proud of you regardless, I promise.*

So, you've completed further education, survived the application process in one piece, received an offer, and *now* it's time to get excited: you're off to university!

It's a time to celebrate, and it's also a time to start making preparations.

Stick with me, because we're coming to the fun part-preparing for the beginning of your independent life...

Chapter Four
ACCOMMODATION

First things first, we need to get a roof over your head. Choosing your accommodation preferences forms one of the first big decisions you'll make about your student life, and if you're living away from home, you'll need to consider whether you'd prefer to be in halls of residence (in university accommodation) or off-campus in student housing.

First year: university accommodation

Universities typically offer student halls of residence or similar accommodation, either on-campus or within a sensible distance in the nearby community, and it's common practice for first year students to opt for this kind of set-up. The chances are you've already had a look around the accommodation that's on offer and have an idea of your preferences, but here are some things to consider from a chronic illness perspective, when choosing your room...

Shared flat or studio?

Most student accommodation is comprised of single rooms, grouped into flats or floors. The number of people in each flat will vary, but students will tend to have their own private room (either with an en-suite or a communal bathroom) and share a kitchen between them. In more modern developments there may even be a communal living area per flat, too. Alternatively, studios may be available. These are self-contained mini apartments which typically consist of a room, bathroom and kitchen all for one individual student.

So, which would be best for you? Let's look at the pros and cons of both...

Shared Flat

Pros	Cons
Usually more sociable environment where it's easy to meet new people	Can be noisier and more hectic
Often more affordable than studio apartments, even those with private en-suite bathrooms	Communal spaces may be more difficult to keep clean
Accommodation for Freshers may be closer to campus or key locations	Individual rooms can be very small with little room for storage
	Unless reasonable adjustments are requested, your room may be up several flights of stairs.

Studio Apartment

Pros	Cons
Offers more privacy	Can be more difficult to meet new people
An individual kitchen may be easier to keep clean or free of allergens	Studios may be significantly more expensive than flat shares
Potentially more storage for medical equipment	You may be more likely to have mature students or more senior individuals as neighbours, who may be less sociable
More space to move around and may feel less confining if you spend a lot of time indoors	

Quiet or non-quiet block?

Some universities offer 'quiet blocks' - groups of flats within one building, designated for those who would prefer a more peaceful environment. With some restrictions and 'no noise after 11pm' rules enforced by porters and university staff, this option could offer a more tranquil setting for those who need it.

Sounds ideal for chronically ill students, right? But you may want to think twice. From talking with others during my own time at university, I found that many of those living in the quiet blocks had been allocated rooms there by default during the UCAS process, rather than opting for them out of choice. As a result, many simply chose to ignore or actively defy the 'quiet' rules.

My Experience

I chose not to opt for a quiet block, although I did question this decision during my first term and even secretly enquired about changing rooms and moving into one. However, I really valued the sociable aspect of my accommodation and was aware that this could be compromised in the quiet rooms.

I later knew I'd made the right decision to stay, because by the end of term, the people in my flat and block were comfortable enough with each other to ask others to keep the noise down... be that politely in advance the night before an exam, or passive-aggressively sticking your head out of the door at 3am because there's drunk people in your corridor playing tennis with an unplugged kettle. *True story.*

There's a possibility these differing stances could lead to hostility and conflict with neighbours, meaning it's something you should think carefully about before pursuing.

Shared bathroom?

As mentioned previously, some standard rooms come with a small en-suite bathroom, whereas others have a shared bathroom system. There can be a significant price difference between the two options, but when coping with numerous symptoms, your own bathroom may well be worth it. All through my research for this book, I couldn't find a single chronically ill student who had shared a bathroom; and I think that fact speaks volumes.

Your own bathroom can take away the need to physically stand and queue, as well as having to factor in extra time for getting ready in case the shower is occupied. Having the facilities to yourself also means you could leave in any mobility aids such as shower stools and grab handles, and if you have multiple chemical sensitivities or allergies, there's less risk of cross-contamination from others' cosmetic products as well.

Ground floor or above?

The majority of student accommodation blocks are formed of many floors, and if the university are aware that you're a disabled student, it tends to be assumed that you'll want the ground floor. In many ways, the ground floor is ideal: I had the ground floor in my first year, and as my block didn't have a lift, it meant no trekking up and down flights of stairs whenever you needed to get anywhere or simply take the bins out.

However, if you're in a more modern building and have a lift, you may like to opt for the higher floors instead. If you're on the top floors, the chances are you won't get as much noise coming through from above.

This is something I personally struggled with throughout my student years, as I inconveniently realised that heavy footsteps and doors slamming from above were one of the primary triggers for my debilitating headaches and migraines. As you can imagine, the completely unjust rage I used to experience every time somebody above me had the *audacity* to come in and out of their own living space and live their own life, made for a really fun time for me...

Moving on swiftly, the other perk to having a higher level room can be a better view out of the window: perhaps a small, insignificant thing for non-disabled students, but if your condition means you spend a lot of time resting in bed, it's little things such as this that can make your environment much more enjoyable and easy to tolerate.

You may not have much control over the external elements of the accommodation you're assigned, however there are also smaller factors that may help you to make the most of your university room.

John, for example, made the following tweaks to ensure his accommodation in Manchester was the safe haven he needed to rest and manage his condition effectively...

I struggle most with my condition when under pressure. This is not ideal when you're studying for a degree, especially when much of your time is spent in a small room in university halls which can, at times, feel quite confining.

During my first year, I was in university halls where I could see my desk (and the tower of textbooks on top of it) from any point in my room. This often made me feel overwhelmed because whenever I was trying to unwind, I could see my textbooks... which always led to me thinking about the work I needed to do that week!

This year, I am making a conscious effort to keep my textbooks and study materials out of sight and only take them out when I'm working. This way, I can ensure I have the calmer atmosphere I need, which should help me feel less overwhelmed and better able to manage my condition. Even though you're at university to study, everybody needs to have a little escape from thinking about work!

Cleaning arrangements?

UK students in university accommodation tend to be a bit indulged during their first year, in that your accommodation may offer cleaners to help maintain hygiene in your living space and communal areas. This is an ideal way of easing young people into independent living and can be particularly handy for chronically ill students, as it's one less thing to worry about spending your valuable energy on as you're settling in.

Whilst it certainly won't completely erase the need for you to clean and tidy yourself, having a proper fortnightly scrub of the kitchen and bathroom by a staff member can be hugely beneficial. I'd strongly advise getting to know the cleaner and earning a place in their good books if you can: if they see that you're making an effort yourself, you're less likely to be held accountable if you have a particularly unhygienic flatmate that spoils it for everybody else. By the end of my first term, Teresa the cleaner and I had really bonded over our shared fondness for reusable tote bags. Absolutely wild scenes.

Anyway, stick with me. We'll discuss some accessible ways of keeping on top of your cleaning and tidying in more depth in Chapter Six.

Catered or self-catered?

We'll also talk more about cooking later on in this book, but one final point to consider when choosing university halls is whether to opt for catered or self-catered options. Different things work for different people, but here are some pros and cons to consider…

Catered accommodation

Pros	Cons
Less need to shop for your own food and plan your meals.	Mealtimes are usually set periods in the day, allowing for less flexibility if you're feeling unwell.
Takes away the exertion of cooking and washing up and leaves you with more usable time and energy per day.	If you have to follow a specific diet, the catering team may not be able to confirm that meals are suitable for you, or give you fewer options to choose from.
Can be a sociable occasion where you can meet and enjoy the company of others.	Dining halls can be a distance away from where you're living. Could you manage it on a tough symptom day?
Tends to result in a tidier shared kitchen, although this space may be shared between an increased number of students in catered blocks.	Increases the price of your accommodation. Is the food you'll be getting good value for money?

Self-catered accommodation

Pros	Cons
You can eat whenever you want, without sticking to set mealtimes.	You'll need to shop for your own food and meal plan, which can be draining on your energy levels.
If you follow a special diet, ensure what you're eating is safe for you.	You'll also need to prepare and cook the food, and clean up yourself afterwards, which again can be time-consuming and energy-draining.
Meals can be prepared in your kitchen, without the need to walk to a separate building and sit at a table.	
Can be easier to budget and make economical choices that fit within your finances.	

Living at Home

Of course, you may decide that living at home rather than moving into student accommodation is the best option for you. Even if doing so would involve commuting to and from contact hours, it may still be that the home-environment that you're used to is most suitable.

These things may not always be black and white, either. **Laura**, for example, technically lived at home, but also moved away for a couple of days at a time during her studies…

My BA Theology, Ministry and Mission course was full-time, but as the hours were split between lectures at university and practical work, which I could complete at home, I was only on campus for approximately two days, every other week. I therefore remained living at home, but on the days I was expected to attend contact hours, I stayed in campus accommodation for the night along with my peers.

Here are some of my tips for splitting living between home and university, when you have a chronic illness:

- o *Plan your time away in advance by prepping yourself mentally and physically. Although you might have the opportunity to rest between lectures, ensure you also reserve energy for the commute, as well as the extra concentration required to listen, learn and interact with peers.*

o *Talk! By speaking to others, such as course directors, they could provide extra assistance to enable you to do your best. For me, this meant having access to a quiet room at lunchtime and allowing me to leave the lecture without question if I felt really unwell. If the university don't know about your requirements, they won't be able to help, so be as open and honest as you can.*

o *Build good relationships with peers. Although those who are leading the course will likely have your best interests at heart, they won't always necessarily be with you if you suddenly need assistance. Once, when I collapsed in a lecture, it was my peers around me who noticed first and were ready to assist.*

To conclude, I feel that splitting my time between home and university worked out well for me. I knew in advance when I needed to stay over and could plan around it, therefore managing to maintain a fairly good level of health throughout my degree. Listen to your body carefully and allow others to help you, and just do your best!

Second year - on or off campus?

One of many bizarre social phenomena for university students is having to decide your living arrangements for the following year so early on: often around the beginning of your second term, even though you're likely still getting to know people. You do have the option to stay on campus in university accommodation, which may make the most sense for you if condition management is going well. Alternatively, you could move into privately rented student housing. Your university can help you begin this process, and many organisations have student letting agents on-site, or details of how and where to contact them. You can usually view properties online, and then arrange a time to go and view them in person.

If you're viewing multiple properties in one day, ensure you communicate your needs to the person arranging this. Sometimes you'll be expected to walk between properties which could be something you find difficult, other times they may have a private mode of transport (such as a minibus) available to take you around.

My Experience: Choosing Housemates

The period of time in which students scramble over student housing and choose who they're going to live with can be difficult. You've only known these people a matter of weeks and yet you're being asked to decide who you can tolerate living with for at least another year.

My best advice would be to think about your personal preferences carefully before approaching anybody. If you have a big group of friends, it can be tempting to try for a huge house all together but think about how this would be on a daily basis. Do those you want to live with have a similar lifestyle to you? Are you likely to see eye to eye in areas such as bills and costs, and are you in agreement on the maximum/minimum rent you'd like to pay per week? Do they have the same approach to cleaning and tidying as you?

I was very fortunate in this sense. I was in a lovely friendship group of 5 girls and 5 guys, so we split down the middle and I lived with the girls (who became some of my best friends) in the same house for two years. Although we didn't live especially close to the boys' house, we stayed together as a group all through our time at university. In fact, even though we're in all corners of the country now we've graduated, we still meet up a few times a year and look forward to seeing each other.

If you do decide to make the move off-campus, as a chronically ill student, it's worth giving thought to the following things:

Is the house accessible? Is there a room suitable for you?

When looking at potential houses, think about its suitability for any of your additional needs. It could be wise to make a little checklist of things to consider when looking around each property, to assess whether or not it fits your unique requirements.

Example checklist:

Can you physically access the house? Is it up any stairs or uneven terrain? Doors can be heavy and prone to sticking, are they easy enough to open? ☐

Is there a bedroom on the ground floor or closer to the entrance for ease of entry and exit? ☐

Are the corridors wide enough to accommodate any mobility aids, and is there ample space to store any medical equipment? ☐

If there was an emergency, would your living quarters be easily accessible? ☐

Is your bedroom near a communal area e.g. living room or kitchen where there's the potential for noise disturbance? ☐

Is your bedroom in close proximity to a bathroom for days when walking or mobility may be an issue? ☐

Is there an outdoor space for you to get some fresh air, even if you don't feel up to properly going out? ☐

My Experience

Remember, I wasn't identifying as chronically ill during my first year of university and was having a relatively 'typical' student experience. I studied full-time and did lots of additional stuff, including teaching dance and choreographing for the university competition teams. When we were looking at houses, I had no idea what was to come within the next year, and I had quite an ironic experience when choosing rooms.

Although we allocated these fairly, based on names out of a hat (due to the rooms being different sizes), I cheekily requested the ground floor so I could do my dance practice and choreography without having to trek to the campus sports centre every time. My friends were understanding enough to grant this request, and it was a good job they did: not because I would be dancing in that room, but because by the end of my first term of second year, I could no longer manage the stairs. Ah, life.

Choose lettings agents wisely, and don't let them mess you around

Once you've found a property, choosing your letting agents is something you'll likely have no control over, but it's something to be mindful of nonetheless.

When my group found the house we wanted, we knew from word of mouth that it was under letting agents who didn't have the best reputation among students. However, because we were prepared for this fact, we were better equipped to handle it: we knew to keep evidence of any issues we had from the very beginning (taking photographs of any discrepancies in the property when you first move in is absolutely essential if you want to eventually get your deposit back), and pester our point of contact until they stepped up and y'know, actually did their job. The *joys* of student housing.

A related element to be aware of much further down the line relates to future house viewings of the property you're in, later on in the academic year. Before you eventually move back out, there will be other groups of students wanting to view the property, the same way you once did. If you're chronically ill, this can again be slightly problematic: there's no use trying to rest when strangers are thundering around your house and wanting to snoop in your bedroom.

Students will usually be informed shortly in advance of any upcoming viewings, however whether or not these are adhered to is a whole other issue. After 5 or 6 bad experiences where we were all incredibly messed around by the letting agents, I eventually took quite an out-of-character stand by locking my bedroom door and physically prohibiting anybody else from coming in, so I could manage my pacing during a crucial essay season. And whilst this didn't make me particularly popular with the letting agents, who probably assumed I was just being a hungover mess, I'd encourage you to have no fear in doing the same.

It's also worth noting here that most letting agents, including student agencies, have a complaints procedure that should be available in your contract or online: the typical process can include writing, signing and dating a letter outlining the issues you're having. However, if things aren't being resolved, don't be afraid to seek advice from your university's welfare team or your local council. You don't have to fight the issue alone.

My Experience

Shortly after we moved into our student property in second year, I found myself in need of the first mobility aid I would purchase: a shower stool. My first choice would have been to have one properly installed in our shared bathroom, so that it could easily be flipped up and down and not be in the way of my other housemates.

However, every time I tried to initiate a conversation with our landlord about this, it fell on deaf ears. They would never even respond to my texts, despite responding to other general queries and my housemate's messages.

At the time, I was so new to disability and struggling too much to put up a fight, so I let it go and purchased a freestanding shower stool instead, that I took responsibility for moving in and out of the shower myself. It wasn't until years later that I realised the landlord's actions were in fact discriminatory, and it's just one more example of a time I wish I'd been more aware of my rights as a tenant.

Distance from university

How far away is where you're living from where you study? Is the distance walkable for you, and if so, are there benches or other places you can stop and have a little rest if necessary?

Alternatively, is there a mode of transport that could help you out? As a disabled student, you may be eligible for a free bus pass or subsidised taxis to get you to and from contact hours: we'll talk more about these elements in later chapters.

How are the local amenities?

The area you're living in can be just as important as the house you're looking at. Does it have a good reputation, and is it residential? Are there places where you can conveniently do your food shop or access any services you need? Some student houses don't have dryers: is there a laundrette nearby? Think about what you might need on a day-to-day basis, and if these things aren't accommodated in your actual house, ensure they're available close by instead.

Accommodation tips and advice

Wherever you opt to live, there are some universal tips and tricks for making your experience away from home as comfortable as possible:

o   When choosing your house or room, identify any noise threats that could interrupt your resting or studying time. If your room overlooks a busy main road or a student pub or club, there's potential for disturbance that you have no control over. In our case, it was our terraced house's living room situated next to the neighbours' living room that was an eyebrow raiser: we had John Legend's *All Of Me* playing at all hours of the day consistently for two years, providing the somewhat unconventional soundtrack to our student life. To this day none of us can listen to that song all the way through.

o   In line with the above, curtains and walls in both university and private accommodation can be inconveniently thin. If you're a light sleeper or have sleep issues related to your condition, investing in eye masks and ear plugs (or proper noise-cancelling headphones) is one of my top overall recommendations for university.

o   Due to safety protocol, most university halls of residence prohibit candles or any equipment that produces a flame in student rooms. If you're a fan of scents or aromatherapy, reed diffusers or Essential Oil Scent Machines may be a suitable alternative. Similarly, many universities have electrical safety requirements to meet: any electrical equipment you bring with you, such as hairdryers or radios, must be visually inspected in accordance with the University's Portable Appliance Testing (PAT) procedures. This tends to take place during the beginning of your first term, so try not to be alarmed to one day find a rogue electrician knocking on your door asking to closely inspect your hair straighteners.

o Know your point of contact in case of emergency. If something happens, who do you call? In university accommodation there will often be porters or a support team, and in private lettings you'll have a landlord. Write down their contact details in advance and keep them somewhere safe. If you find yourself in an unforeseen situation, e.g. the boiler breaking or an electrical fault, having this information easily to hand will ensure you can access support as efficiently as possible.

o Get to know your neighbours. In halls you'll likely encounter flatmates every day and get to know them by default, but when living off-campus, it can be a really nice gesture to say hello to your neighbours. There may be some stigma and hostility from neighbours living near students, so going around and introducing yourself as a group, if it feels safe and appropriate, can be a good way of breaking the ice and opening communication. Or, if that doesn't feel right, you could post them a nice card through their letterbox. You never know when you might need to call upon them.

And now we've got all those essentials out of the way, we can talk about the fun bit; making your room your own. Picking out your bedding and room décor is hands-down one of the most exciting parts of packing and preparing for university. Ensuring your room is your cosy, safe haven is vital, particularly when you're dealing with chronic illness and potentially spending so much of your day in there.

Rooms can often be on the smaller side, so think about your storage needs and where you would like things to be. If you're going into halls, one thing you could do when visiting example rooms on an open day is covertly take measurements (like my stealthy Dad did back in the day!) and think about what could go where. If you have specialist mobility aids or equipment, is there a place they could fit? And if you're having a tough day, is there space nearby to keep some essentials that you could reach, from your bed?

Give some thought to all these things, be prepared, and enjoy the process. Whether you're a cute décor and fairy lights kind of person, or a minimalist and efficiency enthusiast, enjoy making your living space your own and take pride in it... even on the tougher symptom days, a comfortable environment can make all the difference.

Chapter Five
FRESHERS' WEEK

The waiting period between exams and Results Day can feel like it's dragging on until the literal end of time, and yet the final few weeks before you officially begin university tend to fly by. Before you know it, you'll be on your way to your new accommodation with a car packed full to the brim with your life's belongings and playing 'spot the fellow student' as you coast down the A64.

I'll be honest. Your first week, Freshers' Week, can be a challenging one, arguably one of the most challenging periods of the whole experience. But believe me when I say there's so much to look forward to as well…

Move-In Day

Your university will have a move-in process that you'll have been made aware of before you arrive, including when and where to pick up your flat keys and how to find your room. If in doubt, you can always give your accommodation providers a call beforehand to clarify. You may be allocated a slot of time for your arrival, or it might be a free-for-all.

Either way, my best advice would be to arrive as early as possible: not only for the additional time to move your stuff in, but to claim the best shelves and storage spaces in the communal areas too: Not trying to brag or anything, but none of my flatmates had a chance in hell at bagsying the coveted top shelf of the shared fridge. The fact that I stand at a majestic 5'2 is irrelevant.

On move-in day, there'll often be second- or third-year students floating about to help, and they can be a lifeline. When you're going backwards and forwards from the car and moving a lot of stuff into your room, do take advantage of all the help you can get and don't be afraid of asking them to lend a hand.

Often there are trolleys which can help you lug more stuff about in one go, and also make for a handy mode of transport should your legs give up on you. Trust me, nobody would dare mock your makeshift chariot unless they wish they'd thought of it themselves.

Most importantly, keep a hold of your keys/key-card. Many accommodation blocks' main doors automatically lock behind them, so leaving your key-card inside and finding yourself locked out just isn't ideal. Plenty of time for that later on, such as when you're trying to do your laundry at 2am because you've inconveniently run out of underwear for the next day. Definitely not speaking from experience or anything.

With both moving in your belongings and settling into your new room, it can be extremely tempting to over-exert yourself in the hope of getting everything sorted and in its place ASAP. However, I'd strongly advise pacing yourself, and if you can, relying on help from those around you with the more practical tasks. Making the bed is a good job to prioritise, so there's somewhere all ready and waiting for you to have a little lay down whenever you need one.

Depending on the time of day you're moving in, also consider taking your own meals or snacks so you don't have to factor in the energy expenditure for cooking or searching for food whilst you're getting settled.
You'll likely be meeting new people on the same day, so it can be a wise idea to have food already prepared and save up your energy instead.

And a final point about moving in day: if the entire prospect of moving in over one or two days at the same time as everybody else seems completely impractical due to your condition, speak to your accommodation providers. It may be that you can start moving in a day earlier, when things are quieter and more settled. However, if you're prone to nerves or anxiousness, do think about how you would cope with being completely alone in your flat or block. Perhaps there's somebody who could stay with you that night?

<u>Meeting your flatmates</u>

Social media can be a glorious thing, and if you want to, you may be able to find your flatmates online ahead of moving in day.

Many universities will have private pages in which people can post their accommodation and course details, allowing others to connect with them by commenting and private messaging. This can present an ideal opportunity to not only do some thorough researching of their life history up to date, but also start up a conversation and break the ice. Just remember: if you're browsing through all their online profiles and inadvertently forming a judgement about them, the chances are that they'll be doing the same to you. Depending on how regularly you post on social media, it may be a good idea to look through your profile and have a bit of a spring clean in advance.

The chances are, however, that you'll first encounter your flatmates whilst you're moving in.

My Experience

I remember my first online conversation with one of my former flatmates where I managed to naturally mention that I had severe allergies. One of my biggest worries before moving away from home was how others would react to this and whether they would grasp the severity of my condition, so I was beyond relieved when the flatmate in question not only understood, but mentioned that they had similar allergies themselves. There's no joy quite like bonding over mutual allergens.

One of my essential items for Freshers' Week is a doorstop, to hold your door open whilst you're getting settled. Not only will this help on a practical level when you're moving stuff in and out, it'll show others that you're around and make it easier to chat. Having an open door definitely makes somebody appear more approachable, and at the same time, if you do need a bit of privacy or some down-time, you can also close the door to indicate that perhaps you're not up to visitors right now.

Meeting new people can come much easier for some than others, but the important thing to remember is that your new neighbours are likely feeling just as apprehensive as you are. You might be the one to go up to somebody and say hello, or you might prefer to wait until somebody approaches you first. Either way, just smile and be your wonderful self, and you can't go far wrong.

As for disclosing your disability to the people you meet, that's entirely at your discretion, particularly if you have an invisible condition. This is something we'll talk more about in Chapter Seven, but for now, just enjoy getting to know the people around you. You could be seeing people you'll barely utter a word to for the rest of the year, or you could be meeting friends you'll treasure for the rest of your life.

And remember, friendship groups change. If your flatmates aren't your kind of people, no need to panic; fortunately, there are a couple of thousand other potential new friends to meet instead. Personally it took me right up until the final weeks of my first term to really find my tribe, but my goodness, it was worth the wait.

Conversation Starters

I went back and forth over whether to include this short section, concerned that it may come across as patronising. However, I have first-hand experience of the challenges of sustaining conversation with somebody new when the brain-fog strikes: always at the most inconvenient moment, right? If in doubt, here are a few fool-proof topics to help you out when meeting new people:

- o Where are you from? Where's home for you?
- o What subject are you studying?
- o How are you finding the accommodation so far?
- o I like your... [outfit/ hair/ shoes/ face – maybe not the last one]
- o Have you done anything touristy in the town/ city/ campus yet?
- o Are you thinking about joining any clubs or societies?
- o What are your plans for the rest of the week? Are you going to this [event/activity]?

Going 'Out-Out'

Although it's not everything, a big part of university culture is going 'out-out' to clubs and bars. You'll likely have been informed of any themes or fancy-dress requirements beforehand, and if you do choose to go out, you'll probably be following a relaxed itinerary guided by students in upper years.

In this section I wanted to be mindful that the severity of people's conditions can vary dramatically. There may be people reading this who can regularly go out and enjoy doing so, and others for whom clubbing is completely unthinkable. We'll come to alternate events for those who cannot or choose not to go out shortly, but for now, here are my tips for those embracing the nights out with their chronic illness:

o **Pace yourself.** Freshers' Week shenanigans can begin relatively early and finish hideously late. Take your time getting ready and do it in stages, and remember, there's no need to go mad at pre-drinks. You don't have to be the first one in the kitchen or meeting place, the one who's the life of the party from the get-go. By doing things at your own pace, you'll likely have a much more enjoyable night.

o **Ensure your new friends know about any urgent medical needs in advance.** Regardless of whether or not you've disclosed your condition, there may be things people absolutely need to know in case of an emergency. For example, if you carry life-saving medication, do your friends know how and when to use it?

o **Keep taxi numbers and apps saved on your phone in advance.** During Freshers' Week you'll likely have student guides from second or third year around to help you out, but just in case, have your own methods of getting home too.

Freshers' Week is a busy time for taxi drivers, so have as many numbers and apps saved as possible and be prepared to wait for a vehicle to become available. Perfect opportunity to grab some chips from the takeaway and have a well-deserved sit down, if you ask me.

o Consider researching popular clubs and bars beforehand and see if they operate any queue hopping or access card systems. If you have trouble standing up for long periods of time, having to queue can drain your energy before you even get in. Disability identity cards, such as the CredAbility Access Card, could potentially give you a handy queue jump to avoid this situation, as could your Freshers' Week passes/wristbands. Once inside, if you reach a point where queuing for drinks feels impossible, you could easily win-over a new friend by telling them the next round's on you and sending them off to the bar with some cash and your order.

o **Research the local 'nightlife geography'.** It's worth looking at where certain bars and clubs are placed geographically in relation to each other and having a rough idea of where you'll be going that night. In city centres, venues can be more spread out, and a 5-10 minute walk between them may be common practice. Although unconventional, I can only speak for myself when I say making a friend who can give you a piggyback between locations can be an easy and economical solution to the bar-hopping commute. But if that's not for you... there's no harm in booking a cab. If anything, letting your new companions clamber in with you could be what cements your newfound friendship. My friends and I had some of our best university life chats in the back of taxis.

o **If it's cold, take a coat.** Oh my goodness, take a coat. I don't care if it seems uncool or you think you won't need it. I promise, you won't regret it. Most clubs have cloakrooms where you can leave your belongings for a very small fee and no fuss, and the last thing you want when you're waiting around to get home is for the cold to have an impact on your symptoms and make you poorly. Embrace the coat life.

o **Make notes on your phone.** It's no secret that clubs can be extremely loud, making it difficult to communicate even with those immediately around you. If you need to communicate something important; for example if you're not feeling well or you need some air, you could use 'Notes' or a similar function on your phone to type out what you're trying to say, rather than yell over the music. You could even write out and save some phrases in advance, ready to just whip out whenever you need them.

o **Keep an eye on your drinks.** Never leave them unattended, and if you have even the slightest inkling that somebody has tampered with it, don't drink it. The vast majority of students are good eggs who are out to have a good time, but always be vigilant and aware.

o **Remember alcohol is optional**. There's no rule anywhere stating that you have to get tipsy to have a good time. As I'm sure we all know, alcohol and particular medications are not a match made in heaven. However, if for any reason you're self-conscious about not drinking, nobody needs to know that there's no vodka in the coke you order from the bar. On the flip side, if you're on the alcohol, regular water between drinks can be a lifesaver. You should be able to get tap water for free from any location, and keeping hydrated is hands-down the best hangover-reducing tip. Believe me, your next-day self will thank you for it.

o **If your body is telling you it's time to go home, go.** It can be tempting to push yourself and stay out, particularly when you're around new people, but going home before you overdo it could be the difference between you being well enough to do it again the next day, and being stuck in bed feeling terrible. And often, you'll find there are other students who've also had enough and are dying to go home but not wanting to be the one to say it... you could covertly become somebody's hero and saviour by being the one who initiates heading back with a cheeky takeaway instead.

Alternate Freshers' Week/ Alternate Events

It's so easy to assume that university is all about the drinking and going-out culture, and for some it is, but most universities now offer 'alternate events' during Freshers' Week too. These can range from movie nights to comedy events, and they can be a really lovely opportunity to meet like-minded people and socialise in smaller groups. I think we all know it's much easier to have a genuine conversation and make new friends in this kind of setting than trying to yell what A-Levels you studied at each other over ridiculously loud music in a club and nodding enthusiastically as if you had *any* idea what the other person just said.

And don't forget, you have all the time in the day during Freshers' Week too. Health-permitting, you could explore the area and get to know the place you're living or pop out for a sandwich in the university bar: researching accessible points of interest in advance of Freshers' Week could be beneficial here. Alternatively, you could simply invite new friends into your room for a cup of tea and a chat. Even if you're not going out at night, it doesn't have to jeopardise your socialising or the likelihood of forming new relationships. There are so many opportunities during Freshers' Week, even if you're the one creating them yourself.

But by that same token, remember it's completely okay to say 'no' to things too. If there's something you don't feel like doing, or you know you'll need to spend time resting in order to do another thing later on, there's no need to push yourself to do as much as possible. It's a tricky balance: you want to make friends and seem approachable, without compromising your health and burning yourself out early on. If somebody invites you to do something you don't feel up to, my best advice would be to lightly say that you'll give it a miss this time but ask whether you'll see them at [your particular future event] later. Don't forget, a lot of the things you might want to do won't be going anywhere: there's no need to jam everything plus the kitchen sink into one week when you probably have the next three years of your life to experience them as well.

One final point I'd be keen to emphasise here is that if you don't drink, be that for health reasons or otherwise, and you meet anybody who has something to say about that, they simply aren't worth the time of day. You're going to meet a lot of awesome people over the next few years, and anybody who tries to make you feel inferior for any of your choices, this early on, isn't worth wasting your valuable time and energy on. You do you.

The overarching thing to remember is that everybody's Freshers' Week experience is unique, and so it should be. It's all about what works best for you, as **Georgina** discovered during her own Freshers' Week at the University of Kent...

Freshers' Week can be an exciting yet nerve-wracking prospect for any student, but particularly for those with chronic illnesses and disabilities. However, there are several ways to make things easier.

In terms of my actual move-in day, the one bit of advice I wish I could go back and tell myself would be to accept or ask for help: from whoever you can, whenever you can. I naïvely tried to unpack by myself, but in the end my flatmates offered to help, and it ended up being a nice way to bond as we finished the task together.

Speaking of which, meeting my flatmates was by far the most terrifying yet exhilarating part of Freshers' Week for me. My best advice here is to be open and honest with them from day one. Let them know your limits and what they can expect from you and your situation. I exerted most of my energy making friends with my flatmates, as well as the people in my building during Freshers' Week and I'm so glad I did.

So, try your best to get to know people- even if it's just in your accommodation. Freshers' Week can be crazy, but most people will be up for a night-in at some point. Socialising in this way definitely has benefits for chronically ill people, as you don't need to leave your new home to have a good time. You can even head off for a quick nap or lie down in your room whenever you need to! Similarly, pre-drinks parties in your building can be a great way to go 'out-out,' without really going out. I also found that drinking (or more specifically, not being able to drink) wasn't a problem either. There's usually a society for people who don't drink, but regardless, there was never any pressure to drink anyway, so there's no need to let that hold you back from anything you want to do.

As for daytime activities during Freshers' Week, I personally found it helpful to choose which events I wanted to go to at the start of the week, so I could pace myself accordingly. It's also important to prioritise any induction lectures or workshops you have during this time, but if you can, the fun stuff is worth saving energy for too.

Finally, my last tip would be to try not to worry. At this stage in your education, those around you tend to be more mature and inclusive than they may have been at school and will actively show how willing they are to help. Freshers' Week was one of the most fulfilling weeks of my life, so get ready to embrace the excitement in the way that feels right for you.

<u>Freshers' Flu</u>

It's only fair that we take a minute to deal with the dreaded lurgy known as Freshers' Flu.

You're in a new, shared environment surrounded by people from all over the country, who've thoughtfully brought all their various germs with them. Combined with a lack of sleep, poor diet and sometimes psychological factors such as nerves and stress, the result often isn't pretty. Freshers' Flu can take down even the hardiest of students and reduce them to a shivering blanket cocoon of self-pity.

Having no consideration for your social schedule, Freshers' Flu is just one more challenge for you to navigate during your first few weeks of term, and I can completely empathise with anybody who may be feeling anxious about that. When you're chronically ill, coming down with regular illness (or muggle-illness, as I like to call it) can exacerbate your symptoms and take longer to bounce back from. And personally, it was one of the things I was most anxious about throughout my entire time at university. I used to panic that getting ill would set me back and I wouldn't be able to carry on managing on my own, then panic more at the fact I was panicking. And my goodness, that can be an extraordinarily exhausting thing to deal with.

However, anecdotally it seems that Freshers' Flu is much more likely to hit the party animals than anybody else; those people drinking in excess, eating junk and powering through on very little sleep. So, my very best advice would simply be to take care of yourself in the way you're likely already doing to accommodate your condition. By pacing yourself, eating well and listening to your body, as well as maintaining cleanliness where you can and using wipes and hand-gel, you may be *slightly* less likely to become a victim of the student plague. And I know it's so much easier said than done, but for me, try your best not to worry.

If you do happen to fall ill, keeping your diet balanced and healthy, staying nice and hydrated, and getting plenty of rest is good advice to adhere to. Even if sleep is a struggle, complete rest in bed is still beneficial. Be kind to yourself: your body is doing its best to fight off these foreign germs on your behalf, so just take it an hour or a day at a time, and I promise you'll get back to where you want to be. I distinctly remember being utterly miserable in my third week of term (the pesky germs hit me a little later on, when my guard was down), but cosying up with green tea, tinned soup and one of my comfort TV shows made it much more tolerable.

In a completely different league to Freshers' Flu and not to be taken lightly, it's important we talk about meningitis here too. Although meningitis can affect anyone at any time, there are particular bacteria that increase the risk of meningitis in students. Discussing vaccinations can be controversial in the chronic illness community, however current guidance from Public Health England (PHE) encourages all new university entrants up to the age of 25 to be vaccinated with the Meningococcal ACWY (MenACWY) vaccine before term begins. Even if you have already had the MenC vaccine, you should have the MenACWY vaccine, which you can arrange by booking an appointment with your GP. At the very least, it's important to familiarise yourself with the signs and symptoms ahead of Freshers' Week.

Homesickness

It's not uncommon to feel a little uneasy about being away from home, especially when you're chronically ill.

Whether you're missing family and friends or simply the comfort of a familiar environment, your emotions are one hundred per cent valid... and by no means will you be alone in them.

Jenni was no stranger to homesickness when she moved to East Anglia to study BA Drama, but soon found coping mechanisms that suited her condition management...

During university, I mostly felt homesick when I was struggling to look after myself. No matter how proactive you are, being unwell often makes you miss the support system you have at home.

Other times I felt homesick were when I felt I wasn't being understood by others. However, through the beauty of social media, I managed to find other people at my university who had similar conditions to me. We made a group chat so we could vent about the challenges we were facing, knowing that we could all relate to each other. Sometimes, this can be as comforting as phoning home.

A lot of the time, homesickness comes from loneliness. Making friends can be more difficult when you don't have the energy to socialise like other people but finding your 'thing' and keeping occupied is important. For me, it was student radio: it was an easy way to make friends without using too much energy. I saved my spoons so that for an hour and a half each week, I could have fun, listen to music and spend time with like-minded people. When I was feeling homesick on more difficult symptom days, I'd invite people round for a movie night so I could still socialise from bed.

So, my main piece of advice is not to be afraid of asking for help, and to seek support from others. Of course, the huge irony of all of this is that now I've graduated I'm terribly homesick for university!

Take-Home Points About Freshers' Week

Whether you're shooting for a 'typical' Freshers' Week or you've opted for more laid-back alternate events, it pays to be as well-prepared as possible. As mentioned earlier, you'll likely have been notified about any themes or events that require preparation beforehand, and you'll have had the opportunity to get organised... not everybody has a cops and robbers costume conveniently stored in their wardrobe for such an occasion.

However, it's inevitable that you will have forgotten at least one thing you need, and that brings me to my next golden tip: consider signing up for a next-day delivery service, such as Amazon Prime. If you need something quickly, you might not feel well enough to nip out to the shops and get it, especially during Freshers' Week. Being able to easily place an order online and have it come the next day can make *all* the difference, whether it's for a basic toothbrush or a full-blown novelty giraffe costume for the safari night. If there's ever a time to utilise a free-trial or student rate service, it's now.

And my final point about Freshers' Week is this: know that not every week will be this way. People are living away from home for the first time, they're excited, they might be trying to make an impression, and quite honestly, it can be utter carnage. The first few weeks of term might be loud, and chaotic, and noisy, but believe me when I say it can and will calm down. We'll talk more about dealing with uncomfortable situations in coming chapters, but hang in there, get your noise-cancelling headphones on, and do your best to enjoy the ride. There may be stories from these first few weeks that you'll be laughing or eye-rolling about for the rest of your life…

Chapter Six
DAY-TO-DAY LIVING

In the midst of all this excitement, it's important to remain proactive in looking after your health. In this section, we'll first look at taking care of yourself, and then go on to think about managing daily tasks in your living environment.

Medical care

For non-chronically ill students, medical care can be something of an afterthought: something to worry about 'at the time'. However, if you're dealing with any kind of long-term health condition, I urge you to make this your first priority. If there's ever a situation where you're not well, having all the admin sorted in advance will be one less thing to contend with. So, a few tried and tested tips in that area:

- o Register with a GP surgery nearby. Some universities have their own practice, others have them in close proximity. Even if you have great medical care back at home, you can still temporarily register with another surgery in term-time. Many non-disabled students also take advantage of this: it means you don't have to compromise your spot on the patient register at home, and it means you won't be left uncovered either during term or over the holidays. You can register temporarily in England by completing an online form on the NHS website, and doing so will allow details of your medical condition and care to be passed between different GPs and practices as and when it needs to be.

o Find 'your' GP. As I'm sure many of you know all too well, finding a good GP who genuinely understands your condition can be something of a challenge. It might take a few attempts with a few different practitioners, but once you've found The One, it's worth keeping your appointments consistently with them. They'll get to know more about you and your health as you go along, which could make them a really valuable point of contact for so many things in the future. I didn't find 'my' GP until the final term of my first year but thank goodness I did. She turned out to be a lifeline when my health deteriorated, and everything changed.

o   Online patient accounts, such as PatientAccess, can make medical admin considerably easier: you can take care of administrative tasks such as booking appointments and requesting letters over the Internet, rather than having to phone up or visit the surgery in person each time. I'm sure none of you are strangers to the classic 57 minutes of passive-aggressive hold music first thing on a Monday morning.

o   Keep up with prescription requests and refills. If you have repeat prescriptions, you'll know first-hand what a frustrating situation it can be when you're unexpectedly caught short. It might seem like a pain but write down the dates you'll need to put in a new request, always allowing for extra time and wiggle room. Keep this information somewhere you'll see it: perhaps an alert on your phone or a note in your planner?

o   You may like to set up prescription delivery. This is a (generally) free service for anybody who might struggle to get out and pick up their prescriptions at their local pharmacy. You set this up with the branch where your prescription would typically be sent, and once it's received from the GP surgery, they arrange for it to be couriered to you. This can help you save vital energy but do remember to factor in extra time for them to process the request and arrange delivery, to ensure you're never without the medication you need.

My Experience

Some university surgeries offer a 'stay and wait' service for students wanting to see a GP on the day, taking away the need to book an appointment in advance. In theory this can seem like a really good idea, particularly if you feel you need to see somebody urgently.

However, please don't rush into this like I did. The one time I did a stay and wait appointment, I thought I was being smart by getting up at the crack of dawn to make sure I was at the front of the queue. In reality, all that meant was that I was left to stand outside in the cold, among other very ill and potentially contagious students, for a heck of a long time - my health actually took more of a knock from this poor decision-making than it benefitted from the appointment. Learn from Past Pippa's mistakes, guys. At the very least, take a folding chair and flask and act as if you're camping out for Glastonbury tickets rather than prescription drugs...

Mental Health

Taking care of your mental health as a student is equally as important as being mindful of your physical health. University requires young people to speedily adapt to independent living, and when you throw chronic illness into the equation, it's unsurprising that things can feel challenging. We'll discuss where to find support for your mental health in the next chapter, but for now, let's consider how we can be proactive in looking after our emotional wellbeing, and make doing so a daily habit. Over to you, **Louise**…

University can be overwhelming; it certainly was for me. I turned up with a few bags, booze, GHD straighteners, and little idea of what to expect from my new home and life. I was 19 and both physically and mentally unwell. However, in-between and because of my unique struggles, I explored new places, made new friends, learned new things and managed new responsibilities.

No-one can tough their way through mental illness – we can only determine to be kind to ourselves and to do our best. I find that I have to intentionally make space to be kind to myself: establishing a routine gives me a framework for self-compassion. At the start of a new term or year, I print off my module handbooks, make myself a cuppa and prepare by carefully reading through the assignment requirements, and how the module is structured. Now I can plan my time, adding in the deadlines and balancing them with buffer time and rest.

My trick is to use something I call the "rule of three". Long to-do lists are overwhelming so, each morning over coffee, I list only three tasks for the day depending on how I feel. One task for general wellbeing (e.g. cooking a particularly lovely meal, some sort of purposeful movement, quality time with friends, calling the doctor, taking medication), one for my studies (reading, planning, writing, editing or emailing your lecturer) and one for home (tidy up, wash up, food shop or laundry). I've found that doing so helps me maintain a routine I can keep up with.

Most importantly, be proud of yourself. It won't be easy, so be kind to yourself, accept the mistakes and rest when you need to.

Personal care

Whilst it's important to avoid stereotyping all students as the lazy, unhygienic population the media can sometimes present them as, it's true that many non-disabled students don't have to give the same attention to personal care that somebody dealing with long-term illness might.

There are a few ways you can take extra measures to ensure you're fighting fit as possible during your time at university:

o   Ensure you're eating a healthy, balanced diet. We'll talk more about this soon, but it's important to know that you don't have to compromise the quality of the food you eat for the sake of convenience. It can be tough to get the balance right, but being smart about your food prep and eating well will be a lot more economical and beneficial for your immune system than constantly resorting to takeaways, no matter how much the Domino's student deals through the letterbox lure you in...

o   Keep your living space as neat and clean as you can. Having an organised environment can do wonders for your mental health, especially on the days when your physical health is suffering and you're perhaps feeling overwhelmed. And if your flatmates don't share this same approach to cleanliness, say hello to your new best friend; antibacterial hand sanitiser.

o   Look after your sleep hygiene. The typical student may be of a nocturnal nature, but it's important to ensure you're getting enough good quality rest. Sometimes the late nights may suit chronically ill people with insomnia or sleep reversal – after all, even at 3am you won't have to search far for company – but if you're staying up late, try and sleep in to catch up. Surviving on minimal sleep seems to have become a status symbol in recent years, but you really don't need to force yourself to power through and make yourself ill. We all know that good quality sleep, when it blesses us insomniacs with its presence, makes a huge difference to your overall wellbeing.

o   We all have days where getting up and getting dressed can feel out of the question, and in these instances, it can be useful to keep some essentials somewhere reachable from your bed. Having these things nearby for the more difficult days can be a huge help...

Self-care box ideas

o   Dry shampoo for your hair
o   Baby wipes for a quick wash
o   Hand sanitiser and lotion
o   Small handheld fan or handwarmers depending on your temperature regulation habits
o   Bottle of water

- o Non-perishable edibles e.g. biscuits and snack bars
- o Any necessary medication
- o Massage ball for sore muscles or joints
- o Tissues
- o Phone charger
- o Headphones
- o Spare eye-mask and earplugs

So now we've considered the general areas of looking after yourself, let's think about some of the more practical tasks of day-to-day life. Chores can seem daunting, but there are a fair few ways to make them somewhat more achievable. We've got this.

Cooking

Take cooking, for example. If you're self-catering, you'll be planning and preparing three meals a day.
But not only is this do-able, once you get into the swing of things, it may even become enjoyable too. And that's coming from somebody who once managed to sizzle cookies from a child-friendly packet mix to an inedible crisp. It's the things we love that hurt us the most.

Grocery shopping has pros and cons. If you're already out and just want to pick up some fresh food, popping into the local corner store is ideal. If you're doing a big shop, however, walking around the supermarket and carrying the food home can be energy draining and often painful.

Consider an online food shop instead. You can pick what you want from the comfort of your home and have it delivered to your door, so that all you have to do is unpack. If you have allergies or you're following a special diet, online grocery shopping can sometimes offer a bigger selection of free-from items as well. You can also use website tools to save your shopping lists and favourite items, making it an even quicker task for next time. Sharing an order with friends and flatmates means you can split the delivery charge too.

Choose your kitchen equipment well. Lightweight pots and pans are a must, especially if you have sore arms. If you struggle to stand, a perching stool in the kitchen where you can sit whilst preparing or waiting for food to cook can be a big help. You can also get ring pull devices to help open tins, adapted cutlery and tools, and easy-grip scourers for washing up. Another piece of equipment you may want to consider investing in is a slow cooker, where you can prepare food in advance and have it ready and waiting (and smelling delicious) for you at the end of a long day.

My Experience

One piece of kitchen equipment that isn't designed to be adaptive for disabled people but that helped me immensely was a Wi-Fi kettle. Yes, you heard that right. I won this majestic device in a competition and it meant I could boil the kettle using an app on my phone and be notified when it was ready.

It took away the need to stand and wait for the water to boil, which can make such a difference when you have problematic legs. They're not cheap, and if I hadn't won it, I probably couldn't justify buying one for myself, but they may be worth looking into for any fatigue fighters. After all, tea on demand is a staple part of the lifestyle, right?

A more controversial one given the recent emphasis on environmentalism in the UK, but all things considered, **pre-packaged food can be much more convenient** when you're chronically ill and low on energy. For example, pre-packaged salad in a bag saves you from standing and preparing the veg yourself, therefore removing the need for extra equipment and additional washing up too. Seal these bags up well and place half a piece of kitchen roll in opened packets of fruit and veg to soak up moisture and help keep the food fresher for longer.

Have back-up meals ready for the tougher days. Whether you batch cook and freeze leftovers, or purchase ready meals, have options on standby for the days where you just need something quick and easy to whack in and out of the oven before you get back to resting. There was a time where I made the mistake of resorting to takeaways on these occasions, but your body and bank account will thank you for keeping these as a treat and sticking to leftovers and ready meals where you can. Freezer space can be limited, a common and fatal error by accommodation providers who've clearly never lived the student lifestyle, so it may be worth asking if they can provide an extra freezer of your own for additional storage, as a reasonable adjustment.

My Experience

I remember a couple of occasions where I'd wake up in the morning feeling absolutely rotten, knowing I couldn't take painkillers without eating something, but feeling completely incapable of getting to the kitchen. Instead, my angel housemates came to the rescue once again. I felt guilty and awful Whatsapp-ing the group to ask if anybody could drop off some cereal and a cuppa outside the door, so they didn't have to see what I looked like or how bad it was, but I needn't have worried. Not only did they readily lend a hand, they also went to great lengths to achieve five-star presentation on the meal they left me, ready for me to score as if on Come Dine With Me, also accompanied with adorable notes to cheer me up. Those girls.

If you're dealing with allergies, it's important that the people you're living with know about this. Severe allergies mean even the smallest trace of a particular substance can prove fatal, so kitchen cleanliness takes on a whole new level of importance.

Flatmates should be made aware that if they're using that allergen in a shared kitchen, they need to be vigilant about cleaning up and sterilising the space afterwards, and you may also need to take extra precautions yourself. Nobody needs a spontaneous trip to A&E when you have an essay due.

<u>Easy meal ideas</u>

Thinking about your food in advance and making a rough weekly meal plan can help save vital energy, and money too. So, here are some starter meal ideas which you can change and customise to suit your own preferences/ requirements:

- o   Jacket potato with your favourite filling
- o   Beans on toast
- o   Pasta, sauce and veg
- o   Toasties and hot sandwiches
- o   Stir-fry with noodles
- o   Chicken fajitas/ wraps
- o   Quick and easy omelettes

In the lead up to university, it might be a good idea to trial cooking some of these things in advance; not only to check whether you can physically manage it, but to assess any aftermath too. Some people might find it easier to wash up straightaway before the 'payback' hits, others might find it better to pace and have a little rest in-between. Either way, beginning to figure out these things in advance can help you start on the right foot in the student kitchen.

Cleaning

Cleaning can often feel like one of the more daunting parts of independent living – it was one of the things I personally struggled with the most. However, there *are* tips and tricks that can make tasks more manageable.

- o Pacing yourself and managing your activity is key. We live in a world where blitz cleaning and marathon tidying sessions are quickly becoming glorified and trendy, however when you're working with limited energy, you're likely to get more done by tackling things a bit at a time. Break big tasks up into smaller sections and spread them out evenly. Forcing yourself to wait until you're feeling exhausted before you stop is unnecessary and harmful: be kind to yourself instead. Resting *before* you become exhausted is the key to managing on a longer-term basis.

- o When it comes to laundry, some people prefer to do this in smaller chunks to make physically carrying clothes in and out of the machine and hanging them up less of an arduous task. You can also use handwash to individually take care of essentials between washes by leaving them to soak in your sink. However, if you're on campus and paying for washing and drying, doing everything in one load may be the most economical and less energy-consuming option. But if you're mixing colours, for goodness sake, please remember to use a colour catcher. You could really do without replacing your entire wardrobe on a student budget if all your belongings end up accidentally dyed bright purple from your new freshers' week hoodie.

o Figure out where cleaning fits into your daily and weekly routine. Are your symptoms more manageable at certain times of the day? Are there quieter periods where you won't have to worry about getting out of the house later on? These can be ideal times to tackle a small cleaning task. I used to do one job per day, just before I had what was known as my 'big rest' in the afternoon. Such a rock and roll lifestyle, I know.

o If you're sharing a house or living space with friends, you could come up with a system or rota so each of you know who is doing what. With some apprehension, as my health started to decline, I communicated to my housemates that cleaning was becoming a struggle. I explained that I wouldn't be able to manage this specific thing, but what I could do was this other thing instead. Being honest about what you can and cannot manage means that your housemates are aware that even if you can't physically manage bigger tasks, you're still willing to pitch in and help where you can.

o Decide what's worth the cost expenditure and what's worth the energy expenditure. For example, if you're lucky enough to have a dishwasher in your student house, that's great. But if you're paying the bills, you'll know that it costs to put on a load. Ask yourself which is more important to you; the cost of running the dishwasher, or the cost of spending your energy. This can vary on a day to day basis, and again, this may be an area for discussion and compromise with those you're living with. And if you're desperate, it can be handy to keep a stack of recyclable paper plates hidden in your cupboard for the days when washing up is simply out of the question.

o Be prepared to compromise with your own standards too. Keeping clean and tidy is important, but so is your own health. If you do one thing for my benefit, please don't beat yourself up if everything isn't clean and sparkling every day. It doesn't matter if you didn't feel well enough to make your bed before you crawled back into it. At the end of the day, your physical and mental wellbeing should always be the priority.

o   Research adaptive aids and equipment. There have been some amazing technological advances lately that have revolutionised independent living for disabled people. They can come with a hefty price tag and therefore won't be accessible for everybody, but they can last a long time and make a huge difference to your condition management. I've included some of my own finds, along with much more affordable suggestions, below.

Useful Cleaning Aids and Equipment:

Multi-purpose wipes: ideal for giving surfaces a quick wipe down without faffing around with loads of products.

Rubber Gloves: if you're sensitive to chemicals or prone to allergies, have some gloves to hand... no pun intended. Even if you're okay with your own cleaning products, there may be an ingredient in somebody else's that doesn't agree with you.

Sponges on sticks: if you struggle with mobility, you can purchase equipment attached to sticks which allow you to clean areas without having to reach too far.

These are particularly handy for things like showers and baths, but only for giving them a light clean. If something needs a proper scrub, the humble sponge on a stick may be more trouble than it's worth.

Grabber tools: again, if you struggle to bend and reach, long-handled grabbers can make it easier for you to pick up items and put them in their rightful place. Also handy for poking fellow housemates when you want them to pass the biscuits.

Cordless vacuum cleaner: now, these are costly and not for everybody, but hear me out on this one. Cordless hoovers are very light, making them much easier to navigate than traditional hoovers. You may also be interested in the 'robot vacuum cleaners' where you set them down and press a button, and off they go, sauntering about the room hoovering up of their own accord. For bonus entertainment value, I strongly recommend sticking a pair of googly eyes on the front and giving it a name. Most student houses don't allow pets, so Rover the RoboHoover was absolutely the next best thing.

And a final point to make about cooking and cleaning is this: if you've read this section and panicked, because you don't feel you can manage any of these things, stay with me. There are two avenues of practical help that could offer the support you need...

Employing a Personal Assistant or fellow student through Disabled Students Allowance (DSA)

Beth, who studied Biomedical Science at Bangor University, knows that the support she received from PAs allowed her to make the most of her time as a student:

When I was getting ready to go to university, I was referred to a social worker. We discussed my care needs and they assessed how much support or how many hours I would need to live independently, and then we discussed whether direct payments or agency care would be better suited to me. I opted for direct payments because of the increased flexibility in who I hired and when I used my hours.

Once the hours I had been assessed as needing were approved, I was assigned an Independent Living Adviser (ILA) in my home county. Your ILA then assists with everything related to direct payments, including running payroll: all I had to do was let them know how many hours each PA had done. They also helped with the recruitment process by writing a job advert for potential PAs, and they can sit in on interviews too.

When I first started at university, I had recruited a PA via the advert that my ILA wrote. It was only a couple of days before I quickly realised it wasn't quite working. It was difficult trying to organise for outside help to come in around my timetable and social life, especially when she had to travel, and I needed at least 2 calls a day.

Instead, I settled in for a couple of weeks and waited to make friends. I soon became extremely close to my flatmates and decided to approach them: I asked if they would be happy to help me out with tasks such as cooking, cleaning and so on, in exchange for these Direct Payments. Without the three friends who split the hours between them, I honestly would not have graduated university.

They helped me with pretty much everything. They did all the cooking, cleaning, food shopping, and they took me to appointments. They ensured I ate a good meal every day, especially when I was in a bad flare. Once I became more comfortable around them, they even helped with personal care like dressing and showering. Every little thing they did meant that I was able to focus my limited energy on my studies. It also meant that no matter how bad my health was, I knew that I would be able to do the basics and be fed. It gave my parents much more peace of mind too.

In my final year our schedules didn't match up, so I was finding myself at university on my own. I decided to try out agency care to fill the gap and it was a great help: the only thing I struggled with was the lack of flexibility. However, it was still a great comfort to know that I would have someone checking in on me and helping me twice a day.

For anyone going to university who has care needs, I highly recommend looking into Direct Payments. I still use them now. My advice would be to get a referral to a social worker and sort out how many hours you need. If you're struggling without care before you've managed to make friends, then agency care could tide you over. However, in my experience, you can work out who you would trust to be a PA pretty quickly. Then, my best advice would be to just sit them down and be honest with them.

Keeping boundaries between being a friend and an employer can be tricky, but your ILA can help with any official communication. Most people would be happy to help look after a friend, especially with the bonus of being paid for it too. Most importantly of all, ensure you have the support you need to really enjoy your time as a student.

Social Care

DSA can be subjective, and if for any reason you don't receive the support you need, it may be time to look into social care. This could be issued by your local authority, through having a needs assessment where you'll be awarded any support or equipment the authority thinks you're entitled to.

Alternatively, you may choose to do this privately, through an independent agency. This is something I seriously considered when I was struggling with cleaning, and after some thorough research, I found that not all private organisations are as costly as they might initially seem.

I met with an assessor from my chosen agency in my student house and discussed my needs, and we decided on a one-hour domestic visit per fortnight, where somebody would help with hoovering, cleaning and changing my bed: the bigger tasks I simply couldn't do at this point in time. The flexibility of the private organisation meant that I was getting the help I needed without it breaking the bank, and with my student loan I could justify the expense. If you think this could be an option for yourself, I'd recommend doing your research and arranging an initial meeting to help you come to a decision.

Checklist: Things To Arrange Before Starting Uni

Register with GP surgery ☐

Set up online patient services ☐

Arrange a prescription delivery service to your uni address ☐

Prepare a self-care box ☐

Register for online grocery shopping ☐

Plan some potential meal ideas ☐

Make a list of household tasks you can/cannot manage ☐

Research adaptive equipment and hacks ☐

If applicable, look into DSA and social care ☐

Chapter Seven
SOCIAL LIFE

We touched on going 'out-out' earlier, but I cannot emphasise this enough: there is so much more to university life than student nights and sambuca shots. As well as education and learning, university offers a social experience like no other; a student 'bubble', if you will.

It's very easy for me to sit here and tell you not to worry about making friends, but feeling nervous about meeting new people is completely to be expected. The thing to remember is that there's no perfect or 'uniform' student experience, and no right or wrong way to go about socialising. Being your fabulous and authentic self is the very best thing you can do; there's no need to waste valuable energy trying to be somebody you're not. Remember, no matter how outgoing the people around you may seem, there's a very good chance they're as eager to make friends as you are.

Let's first have a look at more organised activities you could get involved with, and then think about socialising more generally as a chronically ill student...

Clubs and societies

A common misconception about university is that the bulk of clubs and societies on offer to students are sport-orientated. Yes, sport is a big part of student life, but as you'll likely know, it's not for everyone. Before my health declined, I was on the university dance and trampolining teams, but I dread to think how hurtling myself into the air and throwing some shapes would end for me these days...

To give you an idea of what's available throughout the year, most universities put on a Freshers' Fair during your first week: an absolutely majestic scrum of enthusiastic students and a heck of a lot of free stuff. As well as collecting all the flimsy pens and badges your heart desires, it's a good chance to go around at your own pace and talk to the people behind the clubs you're interested in.

There's so much more than sport: you may be into crafting, or reading, or as my university proudly presented, the Taylor Swift society. There really is something for everybody.

Societies such as these can be a brilliant way of making friends. In fact, most of them tend to be relaxed in terms of involvement or attendance, making them particularly inclusive for chronically ill people who find it more difficult to commit to regular meet-ups. The beginning of term is the ideal time for trying new things, so if there's something that catches your eye, do give it a go and see how you get on. If it's not for you, there's usually no obligation whatsoever for you to come back next time.

Getting involved with the university

If none of the hobby or activity-based clubs are for you, you may be interested in the more practical societies, relating to the university or the world around us. Many chronically ill young people are particularly socially conscious, and you may like to get involved with Disabled Students' organisations or the Student Union. Using your voice and experiences to improve the lives of others can be such a fulfilling way of spending your time and meeting like-minded friends.

You could even run for a Students' Union position yourself, just like **Chloe** did:

Hi Chloe! Would you like to tell us a bit about yourself?

Hi! In the summer of 2019, I graduated from Leeds Trinity University with a degree in Psychology and Child Development. I have mild Cerebral Palsy, I'm registered as partially sighted and I have Amplified Musculoskeletal Pain Disorder. Outside of university, I love to write my blog, read books and drink coffee!

What made you want to get involved with your Students' Union?

The Students' Union was something that always interested me. I wanted the chance to improve things for other students, but also to broaden the role to include raising disability awareness throughout the university. I knew quite a few people who were already on the student council and they only ever spoke about it positively. And as an introverted extrovert, I love the chance to work with people.

When did you run for your position, and how did you prepare? How did you balance this alongside your studies?

I ran for the position in my third year and it certainly ensured I stayed busy! In preparation, I asked students how their university experience could be improved, and it was through hearing the experiences of others that allowed me to truly connect with the role.

I'm not going to lie; it was a tricky balancing act. I made sure that everything was written down and always put my health and studies first. I found that setting small goals that were realistic allowed me to spread out the work of being the Disabilities' Officer, whilst ensuring I was working towards the goals I had set out.

Have you enjoyed the experience? What have been some of the highlights for you?

Being the Disabilities' Officer at my university was honestly the best thing I ever did. It allowed me to make a difference and raise awareness. I loved the chance to be able to envisage an idea and then make it a reality. It was a pleasure to support so many students.

A massive highlight for me was my campaign 'What does disability mean to you?' which ran throughout Disability History Month. I was able to connect people who were disabled, able-bodied, students or staff. It was a great success and people's answers were more powerful than I had imagined. It was so lovely to just see others so enthusiastic about it.

Also, I was able to secure funding for assistive technology. This was a big project which included a lot of work behind the scenes. To leave university knowing the next cohort of students were able to benefit from the work I did was truly special.

If you could give one piece of advice to chronically ill students considering running for a position themselves, what would it be?

I wanted to make my university the most accessible and disability-friendly place to study, forgetting I had less than a year and still had my health and studies to manage. It's important to be realistic, and for me, this meant focusing on one main project. Overall, I would advise doing what you love – if you are passionate about the work you are doing then this will show!

So, we know there are various things on offer from student societies and the university. But how about socialising on a day-to-day basis, if your condition means you struggle to get out and about?

<u>Making friends and socialising with flatmates</u>

One of the biggest perks of being a student is that you're already surrounded by potential friends: if you're living in student accommodation, you don't even have to spend energy on getting ready and leaving your flat in order to socialise. Although you'll likely be around at least a few people who enjoy a good night out, you'll find that most students (when presented with an alternative option) will be more than glad of a night off. There are dozens of other things you can do together: movie nights with popcorn, games evenings, cocktail or mocktail making, a marathon of your favourite box sets, group baking… the list goes on. And if you've opted for living at home rather than in student accommodation, being proactive in arranging these things yourself is the very best way to meet new people.

Although the above ideas may seem a bit formal or organised at first glance, this can be a blessing in disguise when you're all still settling in and getting to know each other. And in no time at all, you'll no longer need organised activities to enjoy evenings in each other's company.

My Experience

During my second year of university, when my health was arguably at its worst, I was missing out on a lot of social activities with friends. Everything seemed to take place during afternoons and evenings, when naturally, my health tended to be better in the mornings. However, because I had the honour of living with some of my closest friends, we took it upon ourselves to find a solution. And that solution was brunch.

We'd each set aside a morning in our diaries in advance (so that I could rest up and pace myself), where we'd venture into town for some catch-up time and something nice to eat. Afterwards we'd head home, somehow always end up assembled in my bed with snacks in tow and end up talking absolute nonsense for a good few hours. It might seem minor, but looking back, it was little outings and times together like these that kept my spirits up.

It just goes to show that even if there are things that you're potentially not going to be able to join in with, there could be memories to be made in other ways instead: ways that suit you and your health. I might have been missing out on nights out and various other shenanigans, but I did have good friends and an abundance of pancakes, so I think we all know who the real winner is here...

Sex and relationships

We couldn't have a book about student life without considering the topic of sex and relationships: elements of university that are an essential part of the experience for some students, whilst others couldn't be less interested. Either way, it's unsurprising that life with chronic illness can present numerous challenges when it comes to romantic relationships. **Ruby**, who studies at University of Exeter, shares her own thoughts on the subject...

Navigating romantic relationships as a student can be overwhelming. Dating apps, nights out and the potential of meeting the love of your life in a lecture can make a confusing, stressful but ultimately, a fun experience. However, throw in a chronic illness and things get even trickier.

Having dipped my toes into the dating pool as a student, I know that being disabled complicated things slightly. When setting up my Tinder profile, I spent ages debating whether to include my wheelchair in any of my photos. I didn't want that to be the only thing people saw, however it isn't a part of my personality that I want to hide either, so I felt at a loss. In the end I chose to include the wheelchair photos and put my bio as "yes, I use a wheelchair. Yes, you can ask me about it" and that seemed to diffuse any awkwardness.

Dating is scary; opening yourself up to someone is not a simple task. When managing fluctuating health issues, dating, sex and one-night stands are often the last thing on your mind and that is totally normal too. Putting yourself first and essentially being in a relationship with you is so important. You should never feel pressured or like you're missing out just because you are not 'dating'.

When it comes to sex, especially with new people or on a one-night stand, my biggest piece of advice is to just be honest. I think this goes for anyone who is having sex, disabled or not. Be honest about what you like and what you don't, what is uncomfortable and what feels great. But this is even more essential when you have a chronic illness.

The most important thing for me is to tell the person I am sleeping with what I physically can and can't do on that day. Being this open and vulnerable with someone you are dating or someone you've just met on a night out can be terrifying, and it isn't an easy task. But I promise you it's better than not saying anything and your hip dislocating because you were in an uncomfortable position!

If there is one thing that I have learned as a queer, disabled student, it is that communication is key. Being open and honest from the get-go means things will be much more enjoyable for you. Be safe, be honest and have fun.

Dealing with FOMO

Ah, FOMO: The Fear Of Missing Out. This was undoubtedly my biggest hindrance throughout my time as a student and something I struggled with enormously. Even though there's a lot you can do to be proactive and make sure you're included in as much as possible, there may well be occasions where you're simply not well enough to join in. And that can be incredibly tough.

Whilst I sadly don't have a definitive solution to cure the dreaded FOMO, there *are* things you can do to minimise the impact.

Communicate. If you feel you can, pick a tactful moment to talk to the people around you and let them know how you're feeling. And by tactful, I don't mean guilt tripping them right before they go out the door to pre-drinks, but more of a quiet moment the next day when it comes up naturally in conversation, kind of approach. Even though this won't magically allow you to join in, carefully making sure people are aware that you're feeling a little left out (when otherwise they may not have had a clue) can give insight into how things seem through your eyes.

It can also be hugely beneficial to talk to somebody outside of the 'university bubble'.

Being a student can become all-consuming, which is great in so many ways, but talking to those outside of the metaphorical bubble can be so reassuring. As silly as it may seem, sometimes a reminder that life goes on and the world keeps on turning away from all of this can be the best medicine of all. Have a chat with friends about how you're feeling, and just enjoy catching up: it may be just what you need to lift some of the weight off your shoulders.

Mute the social media. Now, social media has numerous positives and can be an utter lifesaver (particularly for us chronically folk) but let me tell you, it's also a FOMO facilitator. I vividly remember occasions where I'd be stuck in bed feeling poorly, scrolling on my phone and seeing endless reminders that everybody else was out having a good time... apparently. And I use the word 'apparently' because this seems like an apt place to remind you that not everything on social media is real, and images alone don't portray somebody's true experiences: it's *so* important to remember that when you're a student.

That's why I'm a big fan of the 'mute' function included on most social media apps nowadays, and why I'd encourage you to have no guilt whatsoever in using it, even on your friends. If there's something you don't want to see, you don't have to see it. Whether it's temporarily muting people's accounts for the duration of an event you didn't make it to, or just muting them for good, your mental health is the most important thing. Hide that content without having to compromise your phone: everybody wins.

Have a self-care plan. I have no idea if this is an actual 'thing', but this is something I took it upon myself to do as a student: I had things in place ready for when I was having a down-day or missing out on something. It could be something as simple as a bar of your favourite chocolate kept aside, or an episode of something you've been wanting to watch, but having things ready for you to enjoy can genuinely lessen the impact of feeling left out. It's so important to be kind to yourself.

Self-care plan ideas

- o   Listen to your favourite playlist on Spotify
- o   Make yourself a cosy nest of blankets to rest in
- o   Start a new series on Netflix
- o   Wear matching underwear, even if you're not leaving the house
- o   Speak to family or friends on the phone, rather than texting
- o   Open the window and let some fresh air in
- o   Plan some nice things to look forward to in the near future

My Experience

One of the evenings that immediately comes to mind when I think about socialising and self-care as a chronically ill student was the evening one of my housemates and I decided to give a spontaneous gathering a miss and stay in. To this day I cannot tell you how and why it happened, but we somehow ended up throwing an impromptu birthday party for two. The fact that it was absolutely nobody's birthday that day was, of course, irrelevant.

We bought cake (a whole cake each, I might add…), lit candles, decorated the living room simply for the sake of it, and spent the evening eating treats and having a jolly old time, rather than going out drinking. Completely bizarre situations like these are some of my favourite university stories, and even thinking about the sheer randomness of it now is making me smile. Co-op cake is seriously underrated.

Dealing with difficult situations

It would be naïve to jump into student life thinking there won't be hurdles along the way. You may find yourself in difficult situations from time to time, and it can be easy to react impulsively without much thought. Whilst there are generally no straightforward answers to these situations, it can help massively to hear the experiences of others. Therefore, I've enlisted the help of Twitter to tackle some potential situations that could occur...

Disputes with flatmates. Living in close proximity to virtual strangers is something that's just expected as part of university life, but when you think about it, it's actually quite a strange phenomenon. Disputes and disagreements can easily arise, over everything from washing up to heating bills to World War Three over who's been drinking the milk.

@ALittleBitKelly: Communicate! Talk to them or talk to your residential advisor. Even if it feels awkward, it is much better to get it sorted! Or if you're worried, text them on the flat group chat so that you've got your other flat mates to back you up.

@_PippaLouise: Always struggled with this! Living with friends has been the best as we aren't afraid to tell each other off. I've also lived with people I don't know and it's so hard not to come across pass agg. Being direct is usually the best option but can be scary and a lot of energy to do

@chxrlottemae: Stand up for yourself, make sure they know how it affects you etc. I always found it's easier to talk to them in person and ask another person you trust for back up if you can

Explaining your health. This is a tough one and a very big topic to broach. That is, if you choose to broach it. What you choose to disclose about your health, if anything, is nobody's business but your own. However, if you do want to explain what life is like with your condition, there are a few ways you could go about it...

@chloeltear: I always made a point of explaining my disability to the people I lived with. Most of the time this was done in the flat group chat. This gave me chance to plan what I was going to say and allowed me to have control over the conversation.

@JenniPettican: I think come up with an easy statement about your condition - @stickmancrips communication cards can make this super simple. And if people want to know more have a go-to blog/video/website you can send people to for further info, so you don't have to explain it loads of times over.

@Lorna_R14: I prefer to do it one-to-one and make it clear they can ask questions, tbh most commonly it's 'how can I best help you'. I explained different things to different people at different times, depending on relevance. It also opens communication for them when needed

Noise complaints. One common situation which takes on new meaning when you're chronically ill is dealing with noise and disruption. Whilst it's accepted that living with students will entail some unwelcome wake-up calls during the night from intoxicated neighbours, if the noise is excessive and affecting your health, you absolutely have the right to do something about it.

@HannahOstMusic: If it's someone you know, calmly have a word with them. Usually people are more than understanding when it comes to health. However, if it continues or it's someone you don't know, see if your university gives any advice. We have security officers to help out!

@_PippaLouise: Definitely make a noise complaint! In uni accommodation there is always someone you can call to make a noise complaint and they'll sort it asap. Living in student housing I think you can make a noise complaint to their landlord and/or local council. Ear plugs are also great.

@JenniPettican: I usually warned flatmates if I had a something big the next day. I'd wait till 12 then ask them personally & if it got worse then call the warden. If its regular, you can move.

My Experience

The one symptom of my chronic illness that consistently plagues me like no other is noise sensitivity. It's not so much how 'loud' sounds are but how 'sharp' they are that really hurts me: things such as doors slamming and drawers banging can honestly feel like somebody is sticking a hot knife deep into my brain, and to this day it's one of the most challenging aspects of my condition management.

It's also a very difficult concept to explain to others, and I'll be honest: I find tackling situations where I need to ask somebody to be mindful of these noise threats to be really difficult. I feel like I'm being unreasonable and that I should just learn to deal with it, even though I know that if the situation were reversed and somebody asked that of me, it obviously wouldn't have made me think any less of them.

I'm including this here because 1) I'm an utter coward and have only ever addressed this issue with my housemates over good old WhatsApp instead of face-to-face, and 2) one thing that marginally helped me and could help those with similar issues are Self-Adhesive Buffer Pads, available to buy online. They're little white stickers you can attach in between drawers and doors to stop them slamming against each other quite as loudly. I'd be lying if I said they'd completely erased the issue and changed my life, but every little helps, hey?

Needing alone time. Conversely, in this section about socialising, it's important to acknowledge that everybody needs down-time too, even more so when you're managing your health. At the beginning of the academic year, many people feel a unique sort of obligation to seem outgoing and be the life of the party, but it's important to know that it's 100% okay not to be the one doing karaoke and shots-shots-shots every night of the week. Alone time is healthy and necessary, particularly in terms of pacing yourself and recharging. So, how do you negotiate that and get the balance right?

@beeettthh: Make the most of the first month/ first year, on most courses (not all) the hours are lower and grades just need to be a pass at this stage, so it's a good time to worry a little less about the work and use any spare energy to make some friends!

@_PippaLouise: I always need time to decompress. I usually get back from the lab and have a bit of alone time and have some food (1-2 hours) and then try and see friends/do activities in the evening. I really need social contact for my mental health, but I also need my daily recharge time too.

@JenniPettican: Monday movie nights were great because I could still be social whilst being in bed. Once I ended up falling asleep and my beautiful friends finished the film

then tucked me in. Take the time you need. People will understand more than you think. X

Most importantly, seek help if you need it. University can be tough for anybody, even more so when you're dealing with a long-term condition. If you're struggling, know that there are people out there who can help. Your university will have a welfare team trained for occasions just like this, who are experts in helping you to move forwards constructively.

Alternatively, if you're not comfortable speaking to somebody at your university or you'd prefer anonymity, there are various resources and helplines out there too. You can find their up-to-date contact details by searching for them online:

<u>Useful helplines and resources</u>

- o **Student Minds** run Peer Support workshops for students facing mental health issues, as well as those supporting friends and other students who are going through a difficult time.
- o **Nightlines** run support services at specific universities, where students can anonymously call in and receive confidential support and advice.
- o **Students Against Depression** is a student-led organisation that provides support and

information concerning various mental health issues.

o For urgent medical issues, you can dial 111 and **NHS Direct** can direct you towards the right services and arrange an ambulance if necessary.

o **Disability Rights UK** run a helpline sponsored by the Snowdon Trust, specifically for issues concerning disabled students.

o The **Money Advice Service** gives free and impartial advice on financial issues and money management, including budgeting at university.

o **The Equality Advisory Support Service** is a government-run initiative for equality and human rights issues, knowledgeable about the rights of disabled students.

Chapter Eight
FINANCES

Whilst not a particularly exciting topic to think about, managing your money as a chronically ill student is incredibly important. I'm sure you'll already be aware of the many extra costs of disability, and how vital it is to be making smart decisions with your money. Let's first ensure you're receiving all the support you're entitled to, then discuss using your finances wisely at university. Pot noodles, anyone?

Money you may be entitled to

To cover tuition and living fees, undergraduates typically go down the student loan route, where you could be entitled to a maintenance loan and a maintenance grant. The award you receive will depend on many factors, including your country of origin, whether you're studying full or part-time, and your household income (if you're disabled and studying for an Open University degree remotely, you may still be entitled to a living loan). You can find more in-depth information on all of these elements (including the repayments system) on the Student Finance Website, as well as a self-test to check your entitlement.

In addition to your base student loan, you may also be eligible for other forms of income:

Grants and scholarships. Grant and scholarship awards come from universities or other awarding bodies and are given to those who meet certain criteria. As well as skill-specific scholarships such as music and sport, there may be more diverse awards on offer too. Your university's website should have a page featuring their grants and scholarships, where you can find out more and submit an application. If you're a current student and struggling financially, many universities offer hardship grants throughout the academic year too.

Claiming benefits. If you're in receipt of disability benefits such as Personal Independence Payments (PIP) or Universal Credit (UC), it's important to know if or how these would be affected by claiming a student loan. The legislation around benefits is murky as it is, and at a time where the system is constantly changing, I'm not even going to attempt to claim knowledge on this one and risk giving incorrect guidance. Instead, let me point you towards Disability Rights UK: their website is full of invaluable and current information, and they have a section all about finances as a disabled student.

Disabled Students Allowance (DSA). DSA, which we've made reference to throughout this book, is awarded by Student Finance. Following assessments with students, financial support is offered for various additional costs related to a person's disability. These can range from adaptive equipment to transport to and from university, and it's important to utilise anything that's offered to you. There have been significant funding cuts to DSA in the last few years, so going into your assessment with a clear idea of what you need and being able to back this up with evidence is essential.

Kristian, who began university with one chronic condition and received a second diagnosis during his first year, has first-hand experience of dealing with extra costs as a disabled student:

In all honesty, I never really thought much about any extra support I'd receive when going to university. However, after speaking with Student Finance England, they advised me that due to having two chronic conditions (Crohns – that was later diagnosed and Type 1 Diabetes) I'd be eligible for DSA (Disability Student Allowance).

Before heading off to Northern Ireland itself to study at Ulster University, I received confirmation of an appointment at Newcastle University, the most convenient location for where I was previously living, to discuss additional support alongside financial help for my course. All of this was simple and was done via email correspondence.

The lady at the interview quickly established that due to my Type 1 Diabetes, I would be entitled to a mini fridge that would be delivered to my new student address, in order to store my insulin. I also explained that I was in the process of seeing a bowel specialist, to which I was awarded five free taxi journeys per year in case I had flare ups whilst on campus. Three months later after returning home following my first semester, I was diagnosed with Crohns disease.

Whilst at university, I was also juggling a part time job at the weekends, but in my second year toward the end of first semester, my health took a turn for the worse due to my Crohns. It was then that I decided to apply for PIP (Personal Independence Payment).

This was a lengthy process that led to an assessor coming to my student address and asking me what I struggled with. For those who don't know, Crohns is a condition that means that the bowel is inflamed which can lead to a variety of symptoms including painful stomach cramps.

After explaining to the assessor that having to pay for extra necessities such as toilet roll and heat for the house, as well as explaining that on bad days I was missing both university and work leading to financial strain, I thought that it was quite clear that as someone who was in need and struggling, I would be awarded a form of PIP. Around a month and a half later I received a letter saying that I had scored zero points on my assessment. I was incredibly upset and following an appeal, I was again turned down. This is unfortunately something that happens often to chronically ill students and demonstrates the serious shortcomings of the current disability benefits system.

Whilst frustrated with this lack of support, making it harder for those with chronic illnesses to live easier day to day lives, my experience of university and Student Finance England itself was very positive, and went some way in addressing the extra costs I faced as a disabled student. My advice to anyone would be reassurance that academic institutions understand the need for those who require extra support and for that reason, don't ever be afraid to ask for it.

My Experience

One of the most helpful parts of my own DSA award was reimbursed taxi costs for travelling to and from university. Living a 20-minute walk (or two buses) away from my contact hours meant that taxis right to the entrances of buildings for contact hours were an essential additional cost because of my disability. Not having these would mean I couldn't attend lectures even when I felt well enough to, putting me at a disadvantage compared to my peers.

So, part of my DSA agreement was that I would use taxis as and when I needed them, ask for signed and dated receipts each time, and claim back for them all in one go at the end of the year. Yes, the extra admin was a pain, but I simply couldn't have justified the costs without this adjustment. But really, can you even put a price on some of the in-depth life chats I somehow ended up having with taxi drivers over those three years?

In short, yes. You absolutely could.

Finding part-time work as a chronically ill student

The chances are that you're going to have your hands full with managing your health whilst studying for a degree, however it's important to acknowledge that some disabled students may want or need to take on part-time work to help make ends meet. Again, you will know your capabilities better than anybody, and you'll be mindful of what you can and cannot safely manage during term-time.

If you're looking for work that's as non-physically demanding as possible, it may be worth talking to your Students Union: many universities offer customer service or research positions that are conducted over the phone or computer, which could make them a particularly accessible option for those with fatigue or mobility issues. Let me introduce you to **Emma**, who decided to seek casual work alongside her studies...

With accommodation, food and transport prices rising, it's not uncommon for students who receive even the maximum maintenance loan to have difficulty making ends meet. That's not even considering spending money on luxuries, sport or society commitments!

I didn't want to panic over money, so I decided to find casual work while studying. Luckily, over the last few years there's been a huge shift towards universities offering more accessible work for students. Besides typical bar work, my university now has vacancies for library assistants. It also employs digital media managers each year, working to boost the university's online presence. Your university's careers service and students' union will often advertise jobs like this, so it's a great place to start.

But what happens once you're employed? How do you juggle your health, your studies, and working?

For me, knowing my capabilities is key. I chafe at any reminder of my limitations, but honestly? I can't manage a full-time job. I couldn't even manage part-time if it was physically demanding. I needed something gentler, and with more flexibility. Before you start searching, think about what it is you personally need from a job: certain hours, certain duties, flexibility... and so on. Be prepared to ruthlessly eliminate any possibility that doesn't fall within those parameters. They aren't good opportunities for you if they'll drain every ounce of energy you have.

Be honest and ask for what you need. Communicating that there's something different about you can sometimes feel uncomfortable, especially when that something means you'll need adjustments, but it's necessary! You have the right to ask for what you need. If you're doing office work, could this be a padded chair? A footstool? Do you need to work close to a bathroom? Rest breaks? Ask for it! Remember that you're not getting an unfair advantage, you're asking for help to be put on the same level as everybody else.

Connect with others. Some companies may have a network for disabled employees, but even if your job doesn't have this, find a group of friendly colleagues. They might not fully understand the difficulty of your health struggles, but they'll be there to empathise with the trials and tribulations of the work itself - and that can be invaluable.

Banish guilt and comparison. You're studying for a degree, you have a health condition to wrangle, and you still want to work? That's incredible, and you should be proud. It can be easy to fall into the trap of pushing yourself too hard, then feeling guilty over suffering the consequences, but take it from me, in the right role with the right adjustments, there's no need for this. You're doing a brilliant job already. You don't need to prove anything.

Finally, consider that no matter how much you struggle with your health, you are worth just as much as anybody else. All things considered, your personal experiences of your condition could even mean you're a more competent, responsible and compassionate employee. Hold your chin up! You deserve to find work you're excited by. So go forth – and enjoy it!

Extra savings

Regardless of whether you're working, every penny counts when you're a student, so it's valuable knowing where you can cut costs and access some cheeky extra savings. Here are a few of my own suggestions:

Student discounts. Arguably one of the best things about being a student, these discounts entitle you to a glorious range of savings on everything from shops and restaurants to local tourist attractions. For some places, a student identity card issued by your university will be evidence enough to qualify you for the savings offered. For others, you may need to join a more formal student discount scheme and use your card from them. For example, the NUS card is one of the more-recognised schemes for students and entitles you to various offers throughout the academic year. Who'd ever say no to a free McFlurry?

Access card. Similarly, it may be worth looking into a disabled access card. These schemes issue you an identity card based on the medical evidence you provide, and they can be a useful and discreet way of demonstrating your needs and avoiding any costs these things may incur, such as pesky charges at public toilets. There are generic access cards such as the CredAbility Access Card (the one I personally have), which detail your access requirements and entitle you to extra support in certain locations listed on their website. Then there are similar schemes for specific activities or organisations: the CEA access card for cinemas is particularly popular among disabled young people.

Carer/companion tickets. Having an access card such as the above may also entitle you to carer or companion tickets for various outings and activities, where any one person accompanying you receives a free or discounted ticket. This means that you're not automatically disadvantaged for requiring a carer or companion to be with you, where you would otherwise have no choice but to pay for the cost of two people. Again, sometimes evidence isn't necessary here: booking theatre tickets for yourself and your companion, for example, generally tends to be relatively straightforward. Other times, having an access card as described above may be necessary to qualify for the discount. In both cases, if your companion receives a free ticket, you could split the costs of the one ticket you've paid for between you, meaning you both get access for half price. Win-win situation.

NHS HC2 Certificate. If you're not already entitled to free prescriptions because of a qualifying medical condition, the NHS Help With Health Costs Scheme can be a blessing for students. You fill out a HC1 form from the NHS website, detailing your circumstances and finances as a student, and if your income is below a certain threshold, you're automatically issued a HC2 certificate. This entitles you to free prescriptions and also other benefits, such as reimbursed travel to and from appointments. Medical costs can quickly add up when you're chronically ill, so the HC2 certificate can be a huge help. If for any reason you don't meet the criteria for the scheme, you could also look into NHS pre-payment cards, where you receive unlimited prescriptions over a set timeframe at a fixed cost per month or year, rather than paying for each prescription individually. These are most cost-effective if you're getting three or more different prescriptions per month.

<u>Dealing with bills</u>

If you're in your first year of university and living in student accommodation, the chances are that most of your living expenses will automatically be included in the cost of your room – although it's important to double-check this and make sure you aren't caught short. If you're living in rented housing, managing your bills is an additional responsibility, and you'll know as well as I do that it's vital to keep on top of things...

Stay organised. Make a list of all your outgoing bills, when payments are due and their estimated costs.

Many people like to do this in a spreadsheet, but it's just as convenient to list them using good old pen and paper and keep them somewhere safe. As well as heating and electricity, think about additional costs such as broadband and your weekly food bill, and don't forget to allow a little extra for socialising or special occasions too.

Consider a joint house bank account. If you're living with friends, there can be many benefits to setting up a joint account between all of you for paying the bills. One person tends to put this account in their name and take responsibility for this, and everybody arranges a direct debit from their own accounts to transfer money into the joint one. When the time comes to pay the bills, it can come straight out of the joint account with no extra faff.

Know how to compromise. Budgeting is vital for the majority of students, and the chances are that your housemates will want to keep bills as low as possible. It's always good to have an open discussion about expenditure: there might be areas where you can all cut back and save some pennies, but it's all relative. Be prepared to compromise and respect each other, but also fight your corner when necessary. If you need to use the dishwasher because you don't feel well enough to wash up, make sure you vocalise that and ensure that those you're living with understand. And of course, others can often benefit too: until you're a student, you may not appreciate just how much of a treat it is to have a dishwasher day…

My Experience

I met some of my closest friends during our first year, and we went on to live together during our second and third years. We were fairly upfront about the house bills and expenses: we all agreed on the timer settings for the heating and for how long we would have it on each day, but we were open to reconsidering it on a day-to-day basis when the colder weather set in.

While my friends tended to be out and about during the week, they knew I was usually at home when the heating was off. On particularly chilly days, I'd message the group chat and ask whether they would mind if I put the heating on for a bit. And of course, it was always okay, but I felt much better for verbalising it first, rather than just making assumptions and switching it on. Having this kind of communication and understanding between the people you're living with means that everybody can remain as happy and involved as possible with the joint expenses.

Be prepared for any emergencies. Student housing can be problematic, and the kind of landlord you end up with can often feel like a bit of a Russian Roulette. Some are amazing and go above and beyond to look after their renters, and others, quite frankly, couldn't care less. If you have issues with any of your housing functions, know who to contact. If you're paying for something that came with the house you're renting and it broke of its own accord, you shouldn't be the one paying for it. If you ever find yourself in a situation like this, document everything you can from the first instance. For example, if the fridge stops working, take pictures and keep a note of the date and time. Not only does this show you're being proactive and you're not to blame, having a timeframe can mean the issue is resolved faster.

My Experience

Another thing you can do to be prepared for emergencies is to have back-up options, but do be wary of these.

Electric heaters can be brilliant to have on standby for if your central heating fails, but my goodness, they aren't kind to your electricity bill. Whilst studying for my Masters, my housemate and I experienced our main radiators malfunctioning in our flat, just as the weather was turning cold. Even after contacting our landlord for weeks and weeks, they never jumped into action to solve it, and we ended up using an electric heater to keep warm.

Even used sparingly, it was a huge additional cost to us, and in hindsight I wish we'd confronted the landlord more strongly about it: after all, the reason we had to resort to that was because they didn't do their duty and sort the radiators out until weeks of pestering later. Gahhhh. Be brave, and if you're not at fault, stand up for yourself. Your bank account could thank you for it.

And if worse comes to worse, I'm certainly no stranger to having a quick blast of the hairdryer on my feet to defrost my toes...

Look into priority schemes. In line with the above, you may be eligible for priority schemes. This means that if there's a wider issue with your water or electricity provider, registering as somebody with additional needs can mean that your issue is resolved as a priority, and you may be entitled to extra support in the meantime. For example, to this day I'm registered with my local water provider as somebody with a long-term condition. If there was ever an issue with my water supply, they're already aware that I couldn't easily just pop out and find help elsewhere. As such, my location would be prioritised and if necessary, they would even deliver bottled water to keep me going in the meantime. These schemes are relatively easy to register for and definitely worthwhile: have a look online or contact your local provider to see what they can do for you.

<u>Budgeting</u>

Whether you use apps or downloadable spreadsheets for keeping track of your money, or simply good old pen and paper, keeping physical track of your regular ingoing and outgoing expenditure in this way can enable you to be as proactive as possible in protecting your pennies. It's always a good idea to have some income set aside in case of emergencies, too.

And as a final point here, I personally believe the key to budgeting as a chronically ill student is knowing what *is* worth the money and what isn't. It's always important to cut costs where you can, but I firmly believe you should never do so at the expense of your health and wellbeing. Even if you too are a novelty onesie enthusiast during the cold season, if you need warming up, take these words right here as your blessing to whack the heating on.

Chapter Nine
STUDYING

So now we've taken care of all the other elements of being a student, we can finally focus on what you're at university primarily to do: study for a degree. With planning, academic support, reasonable adjustments and tips and tricks for learning, let's make sure you have everything you need in order to thrive.

Making a Support Plan

One of the most beneficial actions to take when you become a student is to get yourself a support plan in place. Your university's welfare or disability advisor will usually be responsible for this, so if you haven't heard from them already, it's worth reaching out to them and arranging a meeting. Even if you initially don't think you'll need the support or you won't use it, it's always valuable to have it there to fall back on.

After some discussion with your advisor, you'll come up with a support or learning plan designed to make sure your needs are met. Once you're both happy with it, you'll sign the plan, and this will be made available for your lecturers and course leaders to ensure that accommodations and adjustments are in place wherever possible.

Things to consider implementing in your support plan:

Extended deadlines: the ability to ask for an extension on a piece of work if your condition has prevented you from working at your typical capacity. The extension you're eligible for per format of work will usually be determined in advance, for example a standard one-week extension for a written essay or a two-week extension for a group project. Remember, you'll need to inform lecturers when you intend to use these extensions: they won't automatically be applied to every piece of work you do, and your support plan should outline how to go about accessing them. And, whatever you do, ensure you make clear your intention of using your extended deadline *before* your hand-in day approaches, with as much notice as possible.

Note-taking: having a university PA or assistant to attend lectures with you, take down notes, and provide basic assistance. This can help you to conserve energy and focus on the course content, instead of worrying about getting it all down on paper in real time. It's also worth mentioning that most PowerPoints used during contact hours will be available to students afterwards, so there's no need to furiously scribble away until your hands and brain cramp-up in protest. Some universities also loan out iPads and tablets to students, removing the need to lug a heavier laptop or folder to and from contact hours.

Lenience with attendance: acknowledgement that your condition may affect your ability to physically attend contact hours, and a mutual understanding that when this is the case, you will work from home instead. This is the adjustment I personally pushed for the hardest and benefitted from the most, particularly in terms of pacing and condition management. If you're hoping to implement this for yourself, ensure staff know that you're aware of the need for self-discipline and being proactive when working from home.

Reasonable adjustments in exams: modifications during physical exams to help you perform as well as possible. We'll discuss these in more depth shortly…

Access to libraries: if you're doing distance learning and have an alternative university library closer to home, you may be granted special access to use the resources and facilities there. This can present a good option for distance learners who are well enough to work outside of home and looking for a quiet space to get on with their studies.

Sarah, who studied both BA and MA English at Edge Hill University, has first-hand experience of seeking adjustments to support her academically…

I was 22 when I started university; my health issues meant I had to put my studies on hold so I didn't go when all my friends did. As soon as I applied at Edge Hill I sought out (what was then called) the Inclusions Team to see what support they offered to disabled students. On our first meeting we discussed how my disability would affect me studying, any specialist technology I may need, if I'd require non-medical helpers, and various other things relating to my disability. They helped me apply for Disabled Students Allowance and I no longer worried about getting through my degree on my own.

I received speech recognition software that meant I didn't have to type all my essays; this was extremely helpful when my hands were particularly painful, an ergonomic trackpad mouse and keyboard, which again, saved my hands, a laptop stand, bookstand with light, a portable lumbar support that was small and light enough to carry in my backpack and two incredible learning facilitators that joined me in lectures and seminars taking all my notes for me. Their notes were almost verbatim what the tutors said, they typed them up and emailed them to me the same day, so I had them to work from.

On days when I was in a lot of pain and couldn't concentrate on anything but going home to bed, having my learning facilitator taking notes for me really helped and meant I didn't miss anything important. I also wasn't able to write for long periods of time as my hands would seize up and cause me agony, so having them there meant my notes were comprehensive and consistent.

Then when I got home, I could use the notes they had emailed me alongside whatever piece of assistive technology I chose to help my condition at the time.

I spent many an evening lying in bed with a hot water bottle, with the book I was reading resting on my bookstand on my bedside table, my laptop on the stand on my bed using voice recognition to annotate important passages from the novel I was analysing. I wouldn't have been able to do that without assistive technology. I wouldn't have been able to complete my BA or MA without the support of disability services at my university.

University was difficult, every day was a challenge because I live with chronic pain but the assistance, I received was incredible, and graduating is one of my proudest achievements to date. University is an option for you, there's so many adaptations that I didn't even know existed so I'm sure there'll be something for you, too.

Although your support plan may be automatically circulated among the staff who'll be working with you, my experiences showed me that it's always worth reaching out to them personally too. Upon my return to university after my condition worsened, I made an appointment with my academic course supervisor to discuss my situation face to face, and also give them some more in-depth insight into my condition. As they're likely to be your main point of contact study-wise, they may be able to provide support and insight from a pastoral perspective too. Simply knowing there's somebody among the team of academic course leaders who understands your situation can be hugely beneficial and a weight off your mind.

I also made a point of sending an email to any new tutors or module leaders ahead of timetabled contact hours, introducing myself and briefly explaining my circumstances. This can open a dialogue between the two of you and ensure things are as accessible as possible before the particular course gets underway. There's also no harm in sending occasional emails and updates to staff throughout the term to touch base, especially if you've not been there in person for a while.

An example email to a new lecturer:

Hi [their name],

Hope this finds you well!

My name is [your name] and I'll be participating in your upcoming [module name here] course. I'm just letting you know that I'm a disabled student and have a Support Plan to ensure my needs are met. You should already have access to this, but if for any reason you don't, please do let myself or my disability advisor [name and contact details] know.

My disability means that [your examples here] can sometimes be an issue, so I'd be grateful if you could be mindful of this and my needs could be accommodated wherever possible. If you have any questions, please don't hesitate to contact me, and I look forward to beginning the course soon!

Yours sincerely,
[your name]

My Experience

Although my disability support at university was mostly good, and my academic supervisor was incredible, I do recall one incident with Disability Services that wasn't so positive. Back when I was struggling to physically attend lectures, I asked a disability advisor whether it would be possible for lectures to be recorded and made available later, the way they were for most other courses at the university.

In the email response, it was explained that recording lectures wouldn't be possible due to the rooms in my department not having the technology required. Now, in an ideal world, the next suggestion on their part should have been to move these contact hours to somewhere this request could be accommodated, as a reasonable adjustment. Instead, I was shocked that they came back to me and asked whether I should even be studying if I wasn't able to attend lectures and suggested taking a year out instead.

This was said even in the knowledge that lenience with attendance was part of my Support Plan. At the time I was upset by this but didn't have the time or energy to pursue it further, and I actually don't think the wrongness of it fully registered until much later on. Looking back, I wish I had challenged it: if my academic supervisor was made aware, I'm sure they would have personally advocated for me, and it could have really made a difference to my learning experience. Instead, I taught the majority of my degree to myself, using only PowerPoints and textbooks. If there's something that would vastly improve your ability to study, learn from my hesitancy and fight for it. It's only what you deserve.

Contact Hours

Contact Hours, time spent in university lectures, seminars or tutorials, vary massively between different degree subjects. Whilst some courses prioritise independent study and will therefore not have a great deal of face-to-face teaching per week, others will be more intensive and require full days.

When it comes to attending contact hours, pacing is your best friend. For some people, taking things one day at a time may be the best way to proceed. But for others, it's just as important to look at how your days pan out over the course of the week, and the month. If you have one intensive day per week, you may just be able to physically manage it, but will doing so make you unwell for the next few days? The 'boom and bust' approach can be difficult to manage when you're a student, but by ensuring your workload is as spread out as evenly as possible, you could achieve much more with significantly less payback.

And whilst I'm not advocating skipping lectures if you don't need to, if avoiding the exertion of getting ready and going out means you'll be able to study smarter, it may be worth thinking about. For me personally, attending a day of contact hours one day would mean I wasn't well enough to get any studying done the next day, and sometimes the day after too.

Therefore, I learned that working from home where possible was much easier, and I got through much more studying from my bedroom than I would have done if I'd physically gone into uni. However, think about this in the context of your own life and circumstances, as well as your course and how important the contact hours are for your learning: you'll know what makes most sense for you. I could cope with missing lectures, but if I'd missed my practical statistics tutorials, I would have had no chance of passing my exams. Stats are not for the faint-hearted.

Oh, and another thing to remember? If you're attending contact hours, don't worry too much about spending your energy getting glammed up and looking nice. You're among students: most of them will be crawling in at 9am in a hungover state of disarray anyway.

Although even I would draw the line at rocking up to lectures in pyjamas and a dressing gown, comfy and practical clothing is always a good shout. And who's to say you can't sneak a cheeky thermos and hot water bottle in your bag for a high-pain day?

My Experience

Related to that last point about what constitutes looking presentable during contact hours, I thought I'd mention that I'm yet to meet a single student who regularly ironed their clothes during term time. Ironing is another one of those pesky energy-sapping jobs on the to-do list, but not to worry: I have two hacks for you.

Firstly, we have hanging up slightly creased clothes in the bathroom after you've showered. The steam from the hot water will help some of the wrinkles in your clothes naturally fall out, without any extra exertion from you.

The second, which I was always too scared to try myself, was 'ironing' clothes using hair straighteners. Some friends swore by this one, but personally I was too frightened of burning either the clothes or myself, and I wouldn't particularly recommend it. I think anybody would take the wrinkles over the potential for a raging house fire, right?

Time Out/ Taking A Leave Of Absence (LOA)

Even with support and adjustments, I think we can all agree that life with chronic illness is relentlessly unpredictable. There are good (or better) days, and bad days, sometimes as a result of our actions, other times with no apparent cause whatsoever. With that in mind, there may come a point where taking some time out of your studies is in your best interests.

My Experience

Following my undergraduate degree, I pursued an online learning programme for a two-year MSc in Health Psychology. And though I loved the subject, it's safe to say that the mode of study and complete lack of organisation and professionalism within the university was not only a bitter disappointment, but it completely wrecked my health. I persevered for the first year, but as I reached my final term, my gut was telling me that there was no way I could carry on like this.

Initially, this led to me following the process for a Leave Of Absence (again marvelling at the lack of pastoral support and complete disinterest of my personal supervisor who still didn't know my name. It was a fun time.) and confirming one-year out of my studies, planning to return the year after. However, I think I knew even back then that I was hoping something else would crop up, and thankfully it did. After completing a three-month internship, I was offered my first 'proper' job: one so suitable for my needs and interests that it completely squashed any remaining desire to return to my course. Therefore, I formally withdrew following my year out, and graduated with a Postgraduate Diploma instead of a degree. Even though these decisions weren't made lightly, as they never are when it comes to fluctuating health, to this day I couldn't be more relieved about the choices I made.

I suppose the point I'm making is that if you're ever in doubt about your ability to continue studying, and you're unsure about what the future holds, taking a Leave Of Absence is a good middle ground. It may give you the time you need for your health to get back on track, or it may be the confirmation you need that you'd like to withdraw completely. At the end of the day, it's all about giving yourself choices and doing what's right for you.

Volunteering and Placements

Universities are big on supporting students to enhance their studies, and rightly so. Having relevant experience in your field from volunteering and placements makes you infinitely more employable, and this is something that tends to be emphasised throughout your degree. But when you're chronically ill, how do we make these things manageable?

Meet three of my fabulous friends, who have all experienced volunteering and placements as part of their degree, in various subject disciplines.

First up we have **Charlotte**, De Montfort University student and speech and language therapist (SLT) of the future. With more vocational subjects such as SLT, placements are not only encouraged but a mandatory part of your learning. So how does Charlotte make these placements accessible for her needs, and how can you do the same?

Placements are the glue that holds everything together in my degree; they consolidate all our learning and enable this to be put into practice. Essentially, SLT is a practical, hands-on course. To graduate, we must complete a compulsory number of 'sessions' of supervised clinical placement as set by the Royal College of Speech and Language Therapists (RCSLT). Placements are also my favourite parts of the degree; they remind me of why I wanted to become an SLT in the first place – that magical half hour with a client can make all the hard work worth it.

Placements can feel a tad overwhelming, and it can take a while to get your head around what it is exactly that's going to be tricky, but once this is done you can work with staff to find solutions. My own potential barriers to placements included the length of the days and additional travel time, managing the work and planning that is expected to be done outside of the setting, and where the placements fall in the term, in relation to ongoing contact hours and assessments.

As I had self-disclosed as having a long-term health condition when I enrolled, some of my needs had already been discussed. However, I also focussed on building a relationship with personal tutors: after initially speaking with them, I would reach out by email with some information about the nature of my medical conditions, before moving on to focus on what they and others could do to support me.

For any university location, there are only a certain number of placement offers. We're always told that staff can try their best to make these accommodations, but they can't be guaranteed because they can only give placements that have been offered! Maybe the compromise here is to find another adjustment that can give you (all of, or close to) your needed level of support overall.

However, potential adjustments that could be considered during placements include shorter days with later start times and breaks throughout the day, being based in one building rather than needing to walk between various locations, having some time to visit the setting beforehand, and if necessary, ensuring there are lifts or level entrances. It can also help to think about how best to move yourself and your resources around – I found a wheely-type suitcase perfect for placements! If it's possible, think about the length of the entire placement and explore if you could break it down, too: be that through doing fewer days a week, staggering the days you're physically attending, and considering pre-planned time off midway through the overall placement.

In my experience, I have found that you have to ask specifically for any adjustments rather than assume these things will be taken care of automatically. So, I do lots of thinking myself and I chat to those in a similar situation for tips and tricks beforehand, before approaching superiors. I'd also recommend thinking about how best you can talk to staff about your needs: by email, over the phone, a skype call, or face to face? Is it easier to bring someone with you to the meeting too? Perhaps prep what you would like to say and write down some bullet points.

Finally, ask for staff to later send an email with what you talked about – then you not only have it writing, but you can also have a think and make any more suggestions before you sign off on the plan you have made.

For those dealing with practical elements of courses similar to my own, I like to say, 'there's always a way' and generally, there is. When you really want something and you communicate, remain solution-focussed and work with staff to problem solve – things do work out. Your placement experiences will probably look different to other people's – but if it works for you and your health, that is all the matters.

It's always useful to chat to other students who are on placement too, even if they don't have adjustments. Being able to chat openly about things is so helpful: advice that stands not just for placements, but for university life too!

Next up we have **Poppy**, who recently graduated with a BA in Fashion Promotion & Communication from Southampton Solent University. As a more creative subject, Poppy was required to complete practical work and curate an exhibition to showcase her final project. Here, she shares with us the challenges she faced:

I spent three years studying the business of fashion, including the more hands-on creative side, which on reflection was a lot more than I expected! My first two years involved a broad range of assignments, from event organisation to clothing design. During my final year I specialised in adaptive and accessible fashion: this involved writing a dissertation and producing a final major project on the subject. My final major project involved myself conducting photoshoots, designing a website, writing articles and presenting it via exhibit, print and multiple project books, all whilst housebound.

I experienced so many more inaccessible barriers and frustrations than I should have, and as a result, my work did suffer. I spent my years campaigning for accessibility, for lectures to be recorded or posted online and for the deadline process to be more flexible or inclusive. Unfortunately, however, I got more pushback than change and it did take a physical and mental toll to feel so invisible.

I wish I could share a more positive experience, but I must be frank and realistic: some universities are not yet ready or willing to accommodate chronically ill and disabled students. This especially applies to more creative or hands-on subjects. My degree was hugely impacted by the lack of support I received both before and during university. I was a vulnerable person and had very little guidance on how to deal with difficult situations like discrimination, ableism and advocating for my needs and myself.

However, I urge new students not to be scared off by my tough experience, but instead to learn from it. My experience gives others insight into what to prepare for. Although progress is slow, there are universities who are learning how best to accommodate us.

It's so important that courses, especially creative ones, are willing to make adjustments to help put us on a level playing field. This could include online or skype lectures, to not scrutinize for a lack of attendance, to have flexible assignment briefs or deadlines, and for lecturers to be taught that no two students are the same. If I could repeat my time, knowing what I know now, I would have started by researching universities with a strong support system for chronically ill students.

Most importantly, I would have asked to be put in contact with students with similar illnesses at these universities, to ask for their own opinions. Only these students truly know what life at that university is like, not the fancy brochures! Life with a chronic illness at university is much more effective when we are brought together and find those within the community.

And finally we have **Jess**, who studied BSc Geology at Oxford University. Naturally, fieldwork forms a large component of the programme, and Jess, whose circumstances significantly changed at university, had to tackle this situation head on.

During Freshers' Week, we piled onto a bus and headed to Wales for an introduction into the world of geology and fieldwork. Inevitably, I immediately caught 'Freshers' Flu' once I arrived at university, but I didn't just catch a cold, I caught glandular fever. This marked the beginning of my health deterioration.

Despite recovering from glandular fever, my health remained poor as I continued to study. My college tutor approached me regarding the next upcoming field trip, suggesting I miss it to rest over the vacation, helping me realise my health was priority. I later made the informed decision to defer for the remainder of the academic year and focus on recovery. Although recovery was elusive, after a six-month break I returned to university with my doctors' consent.

Fieldwork is considered central in Geology degrees, allowing students to apply and practice what they've learned in lectures. That said, geology is such a diverse field; it's possible to later direct your studies to specialise in areas better suited to you, requiring little to no fieldwork.

One department-supported accommodation made ready for my return to university was that I wouldn't attend field trips. Instead, borrowing notes from friends, I wrote essays on the geology of the trip locations, and revised at home. Some students might still attend fieldwork with adjustments in place, such as: assistance with carrying kit, taking rest breaks when in the field, or having rest days. Brainstorm with your leaders how to make things work for you, and of course, ensure you have insurance!

But, prioritising your health is paramount; approach trip leaders if you're unable to attend, and ask for any field guides and handouts. See if you may join in evening lectures via Skype or ask that they're recorded so you can review them. Request that team field chats are filmed, and observe any skills taught. Volunteer to produce an essay for each trip to gain a deeper understanding of the area, and possibly ask a leader to later review the material with you.

At the end of second year, rather than studying and mapping an area of choice for an independent project like the other students, I conducted a computer-based project using seismic imaging. As only the second person in my department to have required this alternative project style, it was clear it wasn't the norm; many emails were exchanged as the department seemed unfamiliar with its organisation. It's somewhat unusual for people with chronic illnesses causing physical limitations to study geology...none of us really knew what we were doing! Fortunately, they're now aware of health-related issues associated with field-based work and encourage students to openly discuss their needs with them.

If you have a field-based independent project, plan for a longer trip and schedule rest days. Choose an accessible area, hire off-road vehicles to access field locations or consider using a drone for data collection; allowing you to be 'in the field' without traversing the land. Many universities have drones to borrow at minimal cost, provided you get training. It might even be possible to obtain bursary funding by doing something more innovative like this. Communicate with your department if a field-based project is unsuitable; chat to your supervisor about areas you're keen to study further and organise an alternative desk-based project suited to you! Desk-based projects don't have to be purely that; I worked on my laptop in bed when unable to make it into the department! Nor do they have to be solely computer-based - you could analyse samples in a lab, too.

Whilst missing out on developing field skills, completing a project of this nature gave me experience in industry software rarely taught before postgraduate level. I also developed lab-based skills which I'm more likely to use in the future, thus increasing my employability in an accessible way.

If you're in a position where your ability to participate in field-based work is affected, be open and forthcoming about your capabilities; making adaptations will enable you to overcome challenges you might face. Don't be afraid to self-advocate; share how accessibility can be improved. Your department should embrace inclusivity and make these changes, allowing you to study like any other student and achieve your degree.

Studying and Revision

When it comes to independent study, you'll likely already have an idea of what methods work best for you and your condition. You may be a visual learner who benefits from taking notes, or more practical methods may be most effective for you. Perhaps you're an auditory learner: somebody I know had the genius idea of recording themselves speaking their notes and course content out loud, then listening back to it as a way of learning on tougher symptom days.

My Experience

Academically, the biggest difference between school and university is the emphasis on independent learning. Rather than work from a syllabus as you may have done for your A-Levels, with a definitive list of topics you should be covering, university students are expected to analytically source this information for themselves. No single human being is capable of learning everything possible (trust me), so it's about considering what's worth your time and energy to learn, and what isn't.

You have sole responsibility for your studying, and one of my absolute pet peeves during my own time as a student was people complaining that they 'hadn't been told' this or that, or that their lecturers weren't telling them what they needed to do. It's all about having the initiative to take those steps for yourself.

The good news is that in my experience, most chronically ill people tend to be the best kind of proactive: they take responsibility for all aspects of their life, including learning, meaning that this transition may not be as difficult for you (if you're prepared for it) than for other students. My best advice would be to factor additional time for academic planning into your daily energy expenditure, being as committed to this as you are to your actual studying. It may seem a little scary at first, but once you're into the habit, it'll become easier and easier.

When it comes to revision, I'd recommend starting early and breaking things down into small, manageable chunks. It might seem intuitive, but it can be so easy to inadvertently postpone studying until the last minute and then endure a panic of epic proportions. Take it a little bit at a time and try not to be intimidated by a hefty workload: as long as you're dedicated and prepared, you can do this.

A revision timetable can be a really useful thing, especially in terms of pacing, and many people swear by journals and planners and various systems of organisation. However, I think we all know that the temptation to get carried away with these is real. Spending all your energy on planning and organising rather than your actual studying is a common trap that students, even non-disabled students, fall into. When it comes to planning, a simple grid with an overview of the month, any contact hours and what you intend to revise on particular days is effective enough.

But if you really have to, I *suppose* you can decorate and colour code it to your heart's content.

You'll find out what works best for you, however these everyday study tips from physics student **Verity** may give you some inspiration...

Study and revision often need switching up when you don't have much energy. For me, lectures can be tiring and uncomfortable, but by sitting near an exit you can take a short break if needed. During lectures, I use recording software which lets me highlight any speech I find important, so I can write it down at home without having to listen to the whole lecture again. For me, this amount of 'work' is the perfect balance of keeping focus without being too overwhelming. Obviously, how you're feeling, and the type of lecture determines the best way to take notes. If hand-outs or slides are available, you often don't need to do anything except the odd annotation. However, when there is nothing provided, recording really comes in to play, and doing so means the only things left to worry about writing down (or photographing) are visuals such as equations or diagrams written on the board.

When it comes to studying independently, I personally retain a lot more of what I speak or hear than what I type. Dictation is my best friend: moving from handwriting to speech and typing can make note taking much more efficient. When dictating for my own use, I don't bother with punctuation or corrections until I've finished each section as it distracts from what I'm trying to remember. If having written notes is not important, recording yourself speaking and explaining concepts requires even less energy and can be listened back to- which is often a more fatigue/brain-fog friendly format anyway. You can also do both of these in any comfortable position including lying in bed or moving about rather than constrained to a desk. Other times, pen and paper is the easiest method, and retaining the muscle memory from doing so can be a real bonus. Fine felt-tip pens make writing easier than using a biro, and have the bonus of looking nice, too!

Pacing often means working in small chunks at a time, which can also mean lots of flicking between things to work out where you are and what you're doing. Spending an extra minute before a break writing a brief note of what you need to do next can save a lot of time and help you keep focussed. If there's something you need to check, or you're bogged down in a sentence, just highlight it and move on. When reading, take it paragraph by paragraph and stick a note with a short summary over the top: you only need to process a small amount of information at a time and it's also a good start if you need references later on.

Different methods of studying will suit different people, but I hope these tips from my own experiences help you get started!

Exam Arrangements

If your course involves physical exams, there are various adjustments that can help you through. These elements should already be covered by your support plan, but here are a few you could consider:

Extra time: if your symptoms affect you cognitively, you may be entitled to a set amount of extra time to ensure you're not at a disadvantage. Alternatively, if you struggle with fatigue that impacts your ability to work quickly for sustained periods, the extra time may give you the opportunity for a short rest break during the exam. This one is particularly useful for handwritten, essay-based questions.

Use of a laptop: similarly to the above, if writing under time pressure proves too physically strenuous, especially for those dreaded essay-based exams, you may be able to type your answers out on a standard laptop, provided and regulated by the university, instead.

Additional items: exam conditions at university are similar to schools where students can only have certain items on their desk, and these must be clearly visible. However, if you have any medication or equipment that may be necessary over the duration of the exam, you're allowed to have this on your person too. It's important to make sure staff are aware of this in advance, so you're not having to deal with any confusion on the day. I fondly remember an invigilator admiring my EpiPen shortly before an exam, thinking it was just a fancy biro, until I gently corrected them, and they dropped it like hot coals and promptly scooted off. It's such a joy causing disruption wherever you go.

Adjusted location: the majority of exams are conducted in large groups, various papers taking place at the same time. An alternative to this is asking to take your exam in a smaller, quieter room. This may be individually, so there's just yourself and an invigilator in the room, though some people may find this uncomfortable. There's also in-between ground, which I experienced myself: taking the exam with others, but in a much smaller group. This can mean you're experiencing a calmer environment with reduced background noise and less going on around you, meaning you can focus better on the task at hand.

On the day of your exams, ensure you leave plenty of time to get yourself up and ready at your own pace, and reach your exam location in plenty of time. You don't want to be flapping around and wearing yourself out, and by arriving at the location early, you'll have the chance to have a little rest and familiarise yourself with your surroundings before things get underway.

One thing we frequently hear from disabled students is that it can feel alienating to have extra accommodations in place, to have a different exam set-up to your peers around you, especially if you acquired your condition at an older age. It's important to remember that any additional support you have isn't special attention or a privilege: it's a reasonable adjustment, to put you on a level playing field with those around you. The correct support means that you aren't disadvantaged academically because of your condition, and you, as a disabled student, have every right to this.

And finally, let's talk about good old exam nerves. Us chronically ill folk are notorious for holding ourselves to the highest standards. And that's a good thing, in so many ways, as long as we make sure we're handling these emotions in a safe and productive way.

Leah, who studies at Royal Holloway University, shares the following advice based on her own experiences:

Trying to juggle all the revision and exam stress with a chronic illness can be a phenomenal challenge. As cliché as it is, pacing is what will get you through it. Pace yourself on the revision, pace yourself with how much you're putting your body through, pace yourself in everything during the exam period.

Be open and honest with your tutors/lecturers about what you're going through, as the support of the people around you will be invaluable. Advanced-self-care like meal prepping for yourself can help to make sure you're still eating well even on days you don't have time to cook, and the proper nutrition will support your physical and mental wellbeing. Or if you receive your nutrition another way, make sure you don't skip any doses because you think you don't have time. Your body needs to come first, no matter the exam.

Revision doesn't always have to take place in a classroom or a library - sometimes your bed can be the most productive environment, because you can take better care of yourself while you study. And most importantly, be kind to yourself. It's easy to become frustrated with yourself and your illness when you're trying to achieve the same as your peers, but you're doing the best you can, and that's all anyone can ask for. And I promise, your best is good enough.

My Experience

When it comes to my own academic performance, I've enjoyed moderate success in the past. I've never been one to get full marks or rows of A*s and distinctions, but I've always worked hard and achieved grades I'm happy with.

However, as you may imagine, throwing in a long-term illness diagnosis during your studies does shake things up a little. I don't mind telling you that during my second year, when everything was changing and I was still very much coming to terms with my new diagnosis, my self-motivation was lower than usual, and my grades did suffer as a result. Even though I knew they were below my usual standards, I just put it to the back of my mind. In all honesty, it was probably the least of my worries that year.

The reason I'm telling you this is because it's okay for your grades to fluctuate the same way your condition does. And in the same way they can subtly drop, they can also pick up again too. During my third year, when things had settled down a little, I was able to focus much more on my studies and enjoyed much better results during exams: so much so that I ended up graduating with an unexpected 2:1, a whole classification higher than the solid 2:2 I had my sights set on. The most important thing is just rolling with it (quite literally, in my case), and working to the best of your ability alongside what your needs allow.

Whether it's exams, coursework or day-to-day studying, the overarching thing to remember is that you've got this. A grade or a mark on a written exam has no bearing on your worth or what you've accomplished by studying alongside managing your health: you're facing challenges that many non-disabled students will never know, and no single number or grade on a mark scheme can take that away. For me, please always remember that.

The educational system wasn't designed with chronically ill students in mind, but you're doing the best you can with what you have. And really, what more could anybody ask of you? You've absolutely got this.

So, to sum up…

And now here we are. Whether you picked up this book as somebody considering whether university is right for them or as a student powering through the rest of their degree and in need of some moral support, I really hope this has helped you in some way.

What drove me to initially put this book together was that there didn't seem to be many resources out there that gave chronically ill young people a real idea of what studying for a degree with a long-term condition can be like: both the highs and the lows. Our society is so keen to push young disabled people into education and employment, but it's important that in doing so, we're ensuring these systems are as safe and supportive as possible. I hope you've found this guide a balanced reflection on the challenges we can face, and some of the potential ways around them too.

I'm keen to emphasise that being a chronically ill student *is* doable, but something I wanted to acknowledge one more time before we say goodbye for now is that higher education isn't for everyone. No two people experience chronic illness the same, and even within the same conditions, there are huge variations in people's symptoms and experiences.

In three years' time, you may be collecting your cap and gown and preparing to cross your university's stage as a graduate. You may already be thinking about your next steps and tentatively entering the world of employment. Alternatively, studying for a degree may be the ultimate destination for you: something to be celebrated in its own right, as an additional achievement alongside the full-time role of managing your condition. Being a student isn't just a gateway for future opportunities: as I hope this book has demonstrated, it's a unique experience all in itself.

However, if you've decided that university won't work for you, or if you've begun studying with the best of intentions and had to cease because of your health, I hope you know that that's *completely* okay too; and I'm not just saying that for the sake of it. The education system wasn't built for us, and at the end of the day, your health and wellbeing should always, always be the priority. It's of infinitely more value than any qualification.

For those who are persevering, however, I wish you only the best. Your university years can be the toughest but most awesome years of your life, and you deserve not only a degree, but an incredible social experience and a sense of pride in your achievements.

You have as much right as anybody else to experience university, so do your best, ensure you have the support you need, and enjoy the absolute heck out of it.

So, I think that's goodbye from me for now! If you've enjoyed this book or benefitted from it in any way, please do share it among friends or online, using the hashtag **#ChronicStudying**. I'd absolutely love to hear any of your own university tips or stories, and who knows; sharing them could be hugely beneficial for others too.

Thank you so much for reading, and here's to your own university journey!

Acknowledgements

You know how some people go to bed and dream up their award-winning Oscar speech? My own flight of fancy was to one day write the acknowledgements for a book with my name on it. And although these acknowledgements may look different to how I once pictured them, what with the delightful addition of chronic illness into my life, if anything, it means the following thanks are even more sincere...

First of all, to each and every contributor who generously shared their experiences in this book, I am so grateful for you. Beth, Charli, Charlotte, Chloe, Emma, Georgina, Jenni, Jess, John, Katherine, Kristian, Laura, Leah, Lorna, Melanie, Poppy, Ruby, Sarah A, Sarah S and Verity, your own lived experiences have undoubtedly enriched this read.

To the Daisa & Co team, thank you for being the ethical, sustainable publishers I didn't know I was looking for, and for championing this concept so much that I can now hold it in my hands.

To my university family, known colloquially as SATAN and FREPP, thank you for the most unforgettable three years. To Ffion, Rosie, Ellie, Polly, Alex and Anna in particular, thank you for keeping me smiling. Even now, years later, we find humour in all the various life situations my condition presents, and that makes all the difference.

There isn't a thank you big enough in the world for my best friend Izzy, just for existing as a human being. You believe in me even when I don't believe in myself, help me to live my very best life, and have emergency chips on stand-by for every existential crisis that occurs. There is nobody else I'd rather be a liability with.

And finally, to my Mum and Dad, who not only tolerate my wacky ideas but actively encourage them, this book wouldn't have happened without you. In fact, many of the amazing things that have transformed my life over the last few years wouldn't have happened without you. Thank you for always encouraging me to take the risks, make the most of every opportunity, and most importantly, for providing the multiple cups of tea along the way. I hope I'm making you proud.

Index

BV - #0029 - 280120 - CO - 198/129/11 - PB - 9781916225121